MIRRORS & WINDOWS

MEETING THE STANDARDS

D1414450

Poetry

Unit 6
Reaching Out

Level III

EMC Publishing

ST. PAUL • LOS ANGELES • INDIANAPOLIS

Grade 8 Unit 6 Meeting the Standards

Cover Image Credits: Scene, photo by foureyes www.photo.net/photos/foureyes © 2003; compass, © Don Hammond/Design Pics/CORBIS.

ISBN 978-0-82193-116-5

© 2009 by EMC Publishing, LLC
875 Montreal Way
St. Paul, MN 55102
E-mail: educate@emcp.com
Web site: www.emcp.com

Printed in the United States of America

18 17 16 15 14 13 12 11 10 09   1 2 3 4 5 6 7 8 9 10

Publisher's Note

EMC Publishing's innovative program *Mirrors & Windows: Connecting with Literature* presents a wide variety of rich, diverse, and timeless literature to help students reflect on their own experiences and connect with the world around them. One goal of this program is to ensure that all students reach their maximum potential and meet state standards.

A key component of this program is a *Meeting the Standards* resource for each unit in the textbook. In every *Meeting the Standards* book, you will find a study guide to lead students through the unit, with a practice test formatted to match a standardized test. You will also find dozens of high-quality activities and quizzes for all the selections in the unit.

EMC Publishing is confident that these materials will help you guide your students to mastery of the key literature and language arts skills and concepts measured in your standardized test. To address the needs of individual students, enrich learning, and simplify planning and assessment, you will find many more resources in our other program materials—including *Differentiated Instruction, Exceeding the Standards, Program Planning* and *Assessment*, and Technology Tools.

We are pleased to offer these excellent materials to help students learn to appreciate and understand the wonderful world of literature.

CONTENTS

Introduction

The *Meeting the Standards Unit Resource* supplements for *Mirrors & Windows* provide students with the opportunity to practice and apply the strategies and skills they will need to master state and national language arts standards. For each selection in the student textbook, these resources also supply vocabulary exercises and other activities designed to connect students with the selections and elements of literature.

The lessons in the *Meeting the Standards Unit Resource* are divided into five main categories, as described in this introduction. You will find the lessons listed by category in the Contents pages at the front of the book.

Unit Genre Study Guide, with Practice Test and Master Vocabulary List

Each *Unit Resource* book begins with a Unit Study Guide for the genre, focusing on key language arts standards. This guide provides in-depth study and practice on the genre and its literary elements. Also included are instructions to help students prepare for a standardized test, and a practice test formatted to match that test.

Lessons for Guided and Directed Readings

A step-by-step lesson on how to read the genre accompanies the first selection in each genre. Before-, during-, and after-reading activities and Selection Quizzes are provided for all selections.

The lessons for Guided Readings and Directed Readings offer a range of activities that are rated easy, medium, and difficult; these ratings align with the levels of the Formative Survey questions in the Assessment Guide. These activities can be used to provide differentiated instruction at the appropriate level for your students. For example, for students who are able to answer primarily easy questions, you may want to assign primarily easy activities. The Correlation to Formative Survey Results, which follows this introduction, lists the level for each Guided and Directed Reading activity.

To further differentiate instruction, consider adapting activities for your students. For instance, you may want to add critical-thinking exercises to an easy or medium activity to challenge advanced students, or you may want to offer additional support for a difficult activity if students are having trouble completing it.

Lessons for Comparing Literature Selections

The lessons for Comparing Literature selections in the student textbook emphasize making text-to-text connections. Activities ask students to compare literary elements such as author's purpose, characters, plot, setting, and theme. A Selection Quiz is provided for each selection to help students focus on the selections independently.

Lessons for Independent Readings

Lessons for Independent Readings build on the strategies and skills taught in the unit and offer students more opportunities to practice those strategies and skills. Activities focus on vocabulary practice, literary analysis, and expanded writing instruction. Each lesson ends with a Describe and Critique activity, which helps students review and summarize the selection.

Preparing to Teach the Lessons

Most of the activities in this book are ready to copy and distribute to students. However, some activities will require preparation. For example, you may need to select particular elements from the stories, write lists or cards to distribute to students, or make sure that art supplies or computer stations are available. Be sure to preview each lesson to identify the tasks and materials needed for classroom instruction.

Meeting the Standards

Correlation to Formative Survey Results

The following chart indicates the difficulty level of each Guided Reading Activity and Directed Reading Activity. You can use this chart, in combination with the results of the Formative Survey from the *Assessment Guide*, to identify activities that are appropriate for your students.

Lesson	Activity	Difficulty Level
Guided Readings		
Southbound on the Freeway	Vocabulary: Latin Prefixes, page 19	Easy
	Build Background: Highways in the 1960s, page 20	Easy
	Analyze Literature: Connotation and Diction, page 21	Medium
	Use Reading Skills: Monitor Comprehension, page 22	Medium
	Expository Writing, page 23	Difficult
	Selection Quiz, page 24	Easy
Southern Mansion	Build Background: Antebellum South, page 25	Easy
	Build Background: Slave Narrative, page 26	Medium
	Literary Connection: Literary Terms, page 27	Medium
	Use Reading Strategies: Make Inferences, page 28	Medium
	Expository Writing, page 29	Medium
	Selection Quiz, page 30	Easy
Directed Readings		
Bats	Build Background: Myth or Fact? page 31	Easy
	Use Reading Skills: Identify Author's Purpose, page 32	Medium
	Poet's Attitude toward His Subject, page 33	Medium
	Text-to-Text Connection, page 34	Medium
	Selection Quiz, page 35	Easy
The Choice	Build Background: My Partner, page 36	Easy
	Dorothy Parker's Life, page 37	Medium
	Vocabulary: Nuances, page 38	Medium
	Analyze Literature: Make Judgments, page 39	Medium
	Text-to-Text Connection, page 40	Medium
	Selection Quiz, page 41	Easy

Lesson	Activity	Difficulty Level
Ode to My Socks	Deduction: What Is an Ode? page 42	Medium
	Build Background: *Il Postino*, page 43	Medium
	Vocabulary from Spanish Words, page 44	Easy
	Use Reading Skills: Monitor Comprehension, page 45	Medium
	Expository Writing, page 46	Difficult
	Selection Quiz, page 47	Easy
Casey at the Bat	Build Background: Baseball Quiz, page 48	Easy
	Literary Connection: Allusions, page 49	Easy
	Vocabulary: Synonyms, page 50	Easy
	Literary Connection: Narrative Events, page 51	Easy
	Analyze Literature: Parody, page 52	Medium
	Selection Quiz, page 53	Easy
Paul Revere's Ride	Build Background: Colonial America, page 54	Easy
	Build Background: Revolutionary America in Fiction, page 55	Easy
	Colonial Lexicons, page 56	Easy
	Analyze Literature: Characterization, page 57	Medium
	Text-to-Text Connection, page 58	Medium
	Selection Quiz, page 59	Easy
Grandma Ling	Build Background: Family Resemblances, page 60	Easy
	Vocabulary: Compound Adjectives, page 61	Easy
	Use Reading Skills: Draw Conclusions, page 62	Medium
	Use Reading Strategies: Ask Questions, page 63	Medium
	Text-to-Text Connection, page 64	Easy
	Selection Quiz, page 65	Easy
Exile	Build Background: A Place I Didn't Want to Leave, page 66	Easy
	Build Background: Claim Memories, page 67	Medium
	Analyze Literature: Allusions, page 68	Medium
	Use Reading Strategies: Make Inferences, page 69	Difficult
	Text-to-Text Connection, page 70	Difficult
	Selection Quiz, page 71	Easy

Meeting the Standards   © EMC Publishing, LLC

Poetry Study Guide

Completing this study guide will help you understand and remember the literary element presented in Unit 6—meaning—and review the elements introduced in Unit 5—imagery, figurative language, and sound devices. It will also help you recognize how these elements function in the poems in the unit.

After you read the Understanding feature in Unit 6 in your text, complete the corresponding Understanding section in the study guide. Then complete the two Review sections. This will allow you to write about the key terms and ideas you have learned. Try to answer the questions without referring to the text. The completed section provides an outline of important information that you can use later for review.

After you read all the poems in Unit 6, complete the three Applying sections in the study guide. Refer to the poems as you answer the questions.

After you complete these sections, take the Practice Test. This test is similar to the state assessment reading test you may take. In both tests, you will read passages and answer multiple-choice questions about the passages.

Self-Checklist

Use this checklist to help you track your progress through Unit 6.

CHECKLIST

Literary Comprehension
You should understand and apply the following literary elements:
❑ Meaning
❑ Speaker
❑ Symbolism
You should review and apply the following literary element:
❑ Imagery and Figurative Language
❑ Sound Devices

Reading
You should know the following three parts of the Poetry Reading Model:
❑ Before Reading
❑ During Reading
❑ After Reading

Literary Appreciation
You should understand how to relate the selections to
❑ Other texts you've read
❑ Your own experiences
❑ The world today

Vocabulary
In the Master Vocabulary List at the end of this study guide, put a check mark next to any new words that you learned while reading the selections. How many did you learn?
❑ 10 or more   ❑ 30 or more
❑ 20 or more

Writing
❑ You should be able to write a personal narrative. Your essay should show a grasp of first-person point of view, chronological organization, and plot structure.

Speaking and Listening
❑ You should be able to deliver or listen to a narrative presentation.

Test Practice
❑ You should be able to answer questions that test your writing, revising and editing, and reading skills.

Additional Reading
❑ You should choose a collection of poems to read on your own. See For Your Reading List on page 601 of your textbook.

Understanding Meaning in Poetry

Complete these pages after you read about **meaning, speaker,** and **symbolism** on page 542. Try to answer the questions without looking at your book.

What elements do poets use to give **meaning** to poems? _____

_____

Why is the **meaning** of a poem often challenging to understand? _____

_____

Define elements of **narrator** and **speaker** in the following chart. Use the information from your chart to answer the question below the chart.

	What is it?	**Where is it found?**	**Describe the point of view.**
Narrator			Are events seen from inside or outside the action?
Speaker			Is the speaker's voice the same as the poet's voice?

How are **narrator** and **speaker** similar? How are they different? Explain your answer.

_____

_____

_____

What is a **symbol?** _____

_____

_____

What do the following traditional **symbols** represent?

roses _____   doves _____

roads _____   owls _____

What does it mean to describe a **symbol** as "subjective"? _____

_____

Meeting the Standards

Applying Meaning in Poetry to the Selections

Think about what you have learned about **meaning, speaker,** and **symbolism** in poetry. Then answer the following questions after you have read the selections in Unit 6.

Use the Venn diagram to compare and contrast the **speaker** in "Birdfoot's Grampa" and "The Time We Climbed Snake Mountain." Compare details such as the speaker's point of view, perspective, tone, and main idea or theme.

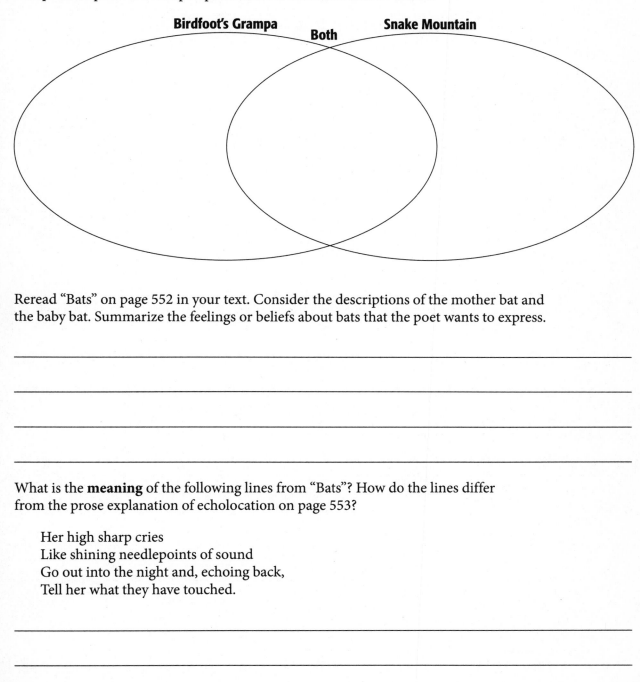

Birdfoot's Grampa   **Both**   **Snake Mountain**

Reread "Bats" on page 552 in your text. Consider the descriptions of the mother bat and the baby bat. Summarize the feelings or beliefs about bats that the poet wants to express.

_____

_____

_____

_____

What is the **meaning** of the following lines from "Bats"? How do the lines differ from the prose explanation of echolocation on page 553?

> Her high sharp cries
> Like shining needlepoints of sound
> Go out into the night and, echoing back,
> Tell her what they have touched.

_____

_____

_____

_____

Reread "Paul Revere's Ride" on page 572. Explain how each of the following details from the poem serves as a **symbol**.

Symbol	Represents	Qualities/Characteristics	What It Adds to Meaning/Mood
Somerset, a British man-of-war (ship)			
tower of Old North Church			
spark struck by Revere's steed			
bridge in Concord town			
Revere's cry of alarm			

Summarize the **meaning** of "The Time We Climbed Snake Mountain." Explain how the poet involved your imagination in communicating this meaning.

_____

_____

_____

_____

_____

_____

_____

Reviewing Imagery and Figurative Language

Think about what you have learned about imagery and figurative language in Units 5 and 6. If you need help, reread page 476 from your textbook.

Complete the sentences.

A poet creates imaginative word pictures by including _____ in his or her poem.

_____ differs from literal language in that it is understood with the imagination.

Write the correct term beside its definition. Then write an example to illustrate the term.

hyperbole	image	metaphor	personification	simile

1. figure of speech that describes an animal, thing, _____ force of nature, or idea as if it were human

   Example: _____

2. figure of speech in which one thing is _____ spoken of as if it were another

   Example: _____

3. an exaggeration used for effect or to make a point _____

   Example: _____

4. language that creates a picture of an object _____ or experience

   Example: _____

5. comparison using the word *like* or *as* _____

   Example: _____

Applying Imagery and Figurative Language to the Selections

List two images from stanza 2 and two images from stanza 3 of "Southern Mansion" and the sense(s) to which they appeal.

Stanza	Image	Sense(s) It Involves
2	1	
	2	
3	1	
	2	

In "The Choice," what qualities of the rejected suitor are emphasized by the **images?** The speaker emphasizes which qualities of the man she chose?

_____

_____

_____

_____

_____

In "Ode to My Socks," list four adjectives the poet uses to describe the socks. Explain what each adjective emphasizes. Tell how each changes the **image** of the socks.

1. _____:_____

_____

2. _____:_____

_____

3. _____:_____

_____

4. _____:_____

_____

Reread stanza 6 of "Casey at the Bat." What do the images in this stanza add to your understanding of Casey's character?

_____

_____

Meeting the Standards

Reread the following lines from "The Midnight Ride of Paul Revere" and "The Cremation of Sam McGee." Complete the chart to show how figurative language adds to the meaning of each poem.

	Kind of Figurative Language	Effect on Mood and Meaning
Examples from "Paul Revere's Ride"		
lines 20–21 (p. 573)		
lines 45–46 (p. 574)		
lines 97–100 (p. 576)		
Examples from "The Cremation of Sam McGee"		
line 14 (p. 595)		
line 18 (p. 595)		
line 33 (p. 595)		

Choose a **figure of speech** from the chart. Explain the imaginative comparison it makes. Tell why you think the poet used it.

_____

_____

_____

_____

_____

_____

Reviewing Sound Devices

Think about what you have learned about sound devices in Unit 5. If you need help, reread page 486 from your textbook.

Why do poets use **sound devices?** _____

_____

_____

What are some of the effects of **sound devices?** _____

_____

_____

Use the terms in the box to complete the sentences below.

alliteration	assonance	consonance	foot
meter	onomatopoeia	rhyme	rhythm
rhyme scheme			

1. Repetition of sounds at the ends of words is _____.

2. Repetition of beginning consonant sounds is _____.

3. A regular and predictable pattern of stressed and unstressed syllables is known as

    _____.

4. Each line of a poem has a(n) _____ created by its stressed and unstressed syllables.

5. Repetition of consonant sounds within or at the ends of words is _____.

6. A word that sounds like the thing it names is an example of _____.

7. A consistent pattern of end rhymes creates a poem's _____.

8. In a poem with regular rhythm, a line is measured in a unit called the _____, consisting of two or more stressed or unstressed syllables.

9. Repetition of vowel sounds within words creates _____.

Applying Sound Devices in the Selections

Think about what you have learned about **sound devices** in poetry. Then complete this page after you have read the selections in Unit 6.

Complete the chart to analyze sound devices in each of the following poems.

Poem	Rhyme Scheme	Description of Meter	Effects of Sound Devices on Poem
"The Choice"			
"Casey at the Bat"			
"Paul Revere's Ride"			
"The Bat"			

Describe the rhythm of "Southbound on the Freeway." Is it written in meter?

Explain your answer. _____

_____

_____

_____

_____

Underline words with sound effects in the following lines from "Grandma Ling"
and "Exile." Then on the lines identify the sound devices used. Explain how they
affect the mood and meaning of each poem.

"Grandma Ling"

> I waited twenty years,
> then sailed back, half way around the world.

_____

_____

_____

_____

_____

"Exile"
> There was no angel to warn me
> of the dangers of looking back.
> Like Lot's wife, I would trade
> my living blood for one last look . . .

_____

_____

_____

_____

_____

> to gaze again on the fishermen of the bay
> dragging their catch in nets glittering
> like pirate gold, to the shore.

_____

_____

_____

_____

_____

_____

Meeting the Standards

Practice Test

Throughout the school years, students take tests to measure how well they meet standards in reading, English/language arts, mathematics, science, and social studies. Students may also take national assessment tests such as NAEP. The national tests include reading tests in which students are asked to read a passage and answer questions to test their understanding of the passage. Some passages on the state reading test will be poetry, like the selections you read in Unit 6.

The practice test on the following pages contains several passages, each followed by two or more multiple-choice questions. Your answer sheet for this practice test is below on this page.

The questions on this practice test focus on meaning, imagery, figurative language, and sound devices—the literary elements you studied or reviewed in this unit. The questions also address these literature standards:

- Students identify the characteristics and purposes of genres such as poetry, fiction, and drama.
- Students recognize and explain themes and symbols.
- Students identify and analyze rhythm, rhyme, sound devices, and figurative language and their effect on meaning and mood.
- Students identify and analyze literary elements such as theme, characterization, setting, plot, and point of view, and elements of figurative language such as simile, metaphor, personification, hyperbole, imagery, symbolism, and allusion.

Practice Test Answer Sheet

Name: _____   Date: _____

Fill in the circle completely for the answer choice you think is best.

1. Ⓐ Ⓑ Ⓒ Ⓓ	8. Ⓐ Ⓑ Ⓒ Ⓓ	15. Ⓐ Ⓑ Ⓒ Ⓓ
2. Ⓐ Ⓑ Ⓒ Ⓓ	9. Ⓐ Ⓑ Ⓒ Ⓓ	16. Ⓐ Ⓑ Ⓒ Ⓓ
3. Ⓐ Ⓑ Ⓒ Ⓓ	10. Ⓐ Ⓑ Ⓒ Ⓓ	17. Ⓐ Ⓑ Ⓒ Ⓓ
4. Ⓐ Ⓑ Ⓒ Ⓓ	11. Ⓐ Ⓑ Ⓒ Ⓓ	18. Ⓐ Ⓑ Ⓒ Ⓓ
5. Ⓐ Ⓑ Ⓒ Ⓓ	12. Ⓐ Ⓑ Ⓒ Ⓓ	19. Ⓐ Ⓑ Ⓒ Ⓓ
6. Ⓐ Ⓑ Ⓒ Ⓓ	13. Ⓐ Ⓑ Ⓒ Ⓓ	20. Ⓐ Ⓑ Ⓒ Ⓓ
7. Ⓐ Ⓑ Ⓒ Ⓓ	14. Ⓐ Ⓑ Ⓒ Ⓓ	

This test has 20 questions. Read each passage/story and choose the best answer for each question. Fill in the circle in the spaces provided for questions 1 through 20 on your answer sheet.

Read the passage below, and answer the questions about what you have read. Mark your answers on your answer sheet.

Orb Weaver
Keisha Moore

Arachne
that proud princess
had no greater task than this
long-legged acrobatic weaver, begun
each day nimbly in darkness, she spins out
her masterpiece. The guylines, strong as steel,
she runs from the hub like spokes. Then she begins
the glistening, beaded thread, a spiral that is death to prey.
At last, she adds her signature—bold zigzag band
on which she rests, head down, long velvet
legs still, waiting. Touched by sun,
her black and gold body holding
both day and night, attuned
to the least shudder,
a pulsing gem.

1. Which of the following best describes the form of "Orb Weaver"?

    (A) a concrete poem

    (B) a metered stanza

    (C) a sonnet

    (D) a haiku

2. The poet compares a spider to all of the following except what?

    (A) an artist

    (B) a weaver

    (C) a jewel

    (D) an acrobat

3. What is the attitude of the speaker toward the spider?

    (A) obsessive

    (B) cheerful

    (C) admiring

    (D) fearful

4. Which of the following best states the poem's theme?

    (A) A careful observer can find artistic beauty everywhere in nature.

    (B) The orb weaver creates an intricate web with artistry and great skill.

    (C) All spiders have an instinct to weave a web to capture insects as prey.

    (D) Arachne was a princess whom Athena changed into a spider in Greek myth.

Read the passage below, and answer the questions about what you have read.
Mark your answers on your answer sheet.

Old Shoes
Nate Vogel

The blue canvas was worn to shreds,
my toes free, air conditioned,
on forays down the gravel road
around the pond's muddy edge,
along dusty pasture paths lined with thistle.

They must have been condemned, no longer
fit for Saturday jaunts to the matinee
or the lunch counter at the five and dime.
One day, sprung from school, I found they'd
simply vanished.

Howling, I would not be appeased
by promises of patent leather shine
or stylish brown loafers. The new tennies,
stiff and white, rubbed cruelly on my toes.
For years, my feet sought those old shoes

their airy comfort, their understanding
that the best friend marches with effortless grace
and perfect rhythm to your every step. I'm sure
the years have magnified their legend. Still,
the longing for those paths, those steps loiter
behind the lesson that a shoe is just a shoe.

5. What has happened in stanza 2?
    (A) The speaker's home has been condemned.
    (B) The speaker has left shoes at school.
    (C) A favorite pair of shoes has been thrown away.
    (D) The speaker enjoys weekend movies and dime stores.

6. The images in the first stanza suggest that the speaker loves what?
    (A) wandering around a farm
    (B) getting dressed up
    (C) cool climates
    (D) swimming and hiking

7. In stanza 3, all of the following happen except which one?

    (A) The speaker refuses to go to town with the family.

    (B) The speaker's parent offers to buy fancy new shoes.

    (C) The speaker cries and will not be consoled.

    (D) The new shoes hurt the speaker's feet.

8. What could the old canvas shoes symbolize?

    (A) the joys of spending time in nature

    (B) childhood's freedom and comfort

    (C) poverty and the hardships it causes

    (D) immaturity and failure to act responsibly

9. Which of the following best describes the speaker's perspective?

    (A) The speaker looks at shoes with a humorous perspective.

    (B) The speaker looks at childhood with a tragic perspective.

    (C) The speaker looks at conflict with a serious perspective.

    (D) The speaker looks at a childhood memory with a nostalgic perspective.

10. Which sound device is used in the poem?

    (A) strict meter

    (B) alliteration

    (C) end rhyme

    (D) slant rhyme

11. "The new tennies, / stiff and white, rubbed cruelly on my toes" is an example of which type of poetic language?

    (A) simile

    (B) consonance

    (C) metaphor

    (D) imagery

12. The poet uses language to contrast which of the following?

    (A) simple and fancy things

    (B) comfortable and uncomfortable things

    (C) family and friends

    (D) childhood and adulthood

Meeting the Standards

Read the passage below, and answer the questions about what you have read.
Mark your answers on your answer sheet.

Electrified Ben
Elizabeth Grier

Old Ben stood calm and scanned the tall June sky
For signs of thunder-gust. His son stood by.
In his hands rested a most unlikely means—
Silk tied to cedar—to capture fiery streams.
Except it bore atop a pointed wire
Down which he hoped to draw electric fire.

Into the burgeoning wind they raised the kite.
It sprang toward racing clouds. Ben felt the bite
Of the twine, as the fierce wind caught and tore
At its slight toy. The heart of storm soon bore
Down, furious and freighted with a charge
That surged and roared and circled like a large

Dragon parched and famished for new meat.
Here was the stuff the old man found so sweet!
The world wondrous with such mysterious power
Harnessed by devices, brought to flower
And made a servant to the needs of all mankind.
This was the key lifelong he sought to find.

So when the fire came streaming down the wet
Line and into the bright key, he knew, and yet
He raised a knuckle, for he had to touch
The kindled magic. Science compels this much.
Nonetheless, surely the noble spirit harked
That day, itself it was that flew and filled and sparked.

13. Which of the following best describes "Electrified Ben"?

    (A) The poem contains regular rhyme and meter.

    (B) The poem no sound effects.

    (C) The poem has a set rhyme scheme but no rhythm.

    (D) The poem expresses the speaker's personal emotions.

14. Which of the following illustrates simile?

    (A) line 7

    (B) lines 10–13

    (C) line 15

    (D) lines 19–21

15. Which object symbolizes the harnessing power of science?
    (A) the dragon
    (B) the glowing key
    (C) the June storm
    (D) Ben's son

16. Which important idea about Ben Franklin is expressed in the poem?
    (A) He was like a child when it came to being curious.
    (B) He took chances when he thought it was necessary.
    (C) He was a clever and practical scientist and statesman.
    (D) He used science to explore and help people.

17. The fire "streaming down the wet / Line" refers to which of the following?
    (A) a scientist's inspiration
    (B) superheated water
    (C) electric current
    (D) the pride of a scientist in his achievement

18. The roaring dragon is best explained as a symbol of what?
    (A) supernatural fear
    (B) opposition by superstitious people
    (C) American importance and might
    (D) the untamed and unexplained forces in nature

19. Which sound device is not present in this poem?
    (A) end rhyme
    (B) meter
    (C) alliteration
    (D) internal rhyme

20. What do the last two lines of the poem suggest?
    (A) Franklin was electrocuted by lightning.
    (B) The dragon was transformed into a "noble spirit."
    (C) Franklin was elated by the success of his experiment.
    (D) The kite was destroyed completely by electric current.

Master Vocabulary List

aloft, 573
decrepit, 562
defiance, 577
diagram, 544
flutter, 552
glimmer, 558
gnat, 552
haughty, 569

impulse, 563
lace, 558
mooring, 573
muffled, 573
multitude, 568
rafter, 552
recoil, 568
remorse, 563

sacred, 563
shade, 549
sheen, 558
smolder, 558
somber, 574
stricken, 568
transparent, 544
tumult, 569

Southbound on the Freeway, page 543

Vocabulary: Latin Prefixes

A. The vocabulary word "transparent" comes from the Latin prefix *trans-*, meaning "across," "beyond," or "through," and *parere*, "to show oneself." Write the letter of the correct root that is added to the prefix *trans-* on the line next to the matching vocabulary word. Use your dictionary skills in order to look up any words you still do not understand after taking the Latin root into consideration.

_____1. transmit

_____2. transparent

_____3. transcribe

_____4. transfusion

_____5. transaction

A. *parere*: to show oneself
B. *fundere*: to pour
C. *scribere*: to write
D. *agere*: to act as an agent
E. *mittere*: to send

B. Fill in the blank with the word from the box that best completes each sentence.

transparent	transfusion	transmit	transcribe	transaction

6. After the car accident, Mr. Petersen had to have a blood _____.

7. The music professor's efforts to _____ the Appalachian song were hindered by scratches on the one surviving album.

8. The business _____ went smoothly and Ms. Bennett ended up with another coffee shop in her portfolio.

9. The army captain decided to _____ his orders to his soldiers on a different radio frequency so that the enemy would not detect it.

10. The dress material was so _____ that the seamstress had to add a lining.

BEFORE READING

Southbound on the Freeway, page 543

Build Background: Highways in the 1960s

A. At the time this poem was written, highway travel and car production were expanding enormously. Type "Interstate Highway System," using your favorite search engine, to find a Web site that will help you answer these questions.

1. What was the name of the legislation that was passed in 1956 that authorized the construction of the Interstate Highway System?

_____

2. Who was the president of the United States at that time?

_____

3. Which branch of manufacturing lobbied for the Interstate Highway System?

_____

4. What were the advantages for the military in having such a system?

_____

5. How was this project paid for?

_____

B. Working with a partner, answer questions about the interstate highway in your region.

6. What is the name of the interstate that goes through your region?

_____

7. Is yours an east-west highway or a north-south highway?

_____

8. Which type of highway has even numbers? Odd numbers?

_____

9. What color are the signs?

_____

10. How are the exit signs labeled?

_____

BEFORE READING

20 LEVEL III, UNIT 6 *Meeting the Standards* © EMC Publishing, LLC

Southbound on the Freeway, page 543

Analyze Literature: Connotation and Diction

The **connotation** of a word is the set of ideas or emotional associations it suggests in addition to its actual meaning. **Diction**, when applied to writing, refers to the author's choice of words.

A. Circle the connotation for each word on the left that you think the poet intended when she wrote the poem.

1. tourist: someone not invested in a place   someone on vacation having fun
2. Orbitville: a small planet   a major planet
3. creature: a monster   a life form
4. special: being in some way superior   individual
5. shadowy: dark   indicating a mystery
6. guts/brains: courage/intelligence   body parts

B. What does the poet's diction reveal about the tourist from Orbitville? What does the poet's diction reveal about life on Earth? Answer these questions in a paragraph.

_____

_____

_____

_____

_____

_____

_____

_____

_____

_____

_____

_____

_____

DURING READING

Southbound on the Freeway, page 543

Use Reading Skills: Monitor Comprehension

Fill in the blank with the word from the box that best completes each sentence.

police car	monologue	onomatopoeia
people	car lights	freeway
snake	human	alien
tires		

1. The tourist from Orbitville is a(n) _____.

2. Starting with line 3, the poem is in the form of a(n) _____.

3. The description "metal and glass" in line 4 indicates the tourist is not looking at
   _____ life on Earth.

4. The description of "round" feet in line 7 indicates the tourist is observing _____.

5. The "white lines" in line 10 indicate a(n) _____.

6. The four eyes of the creature are _____.

7. The car with "a red eye turning/on the top of his head" is a(n) _____.

8. The verb "hiss" in line 21 is an example of a sound device called _____.

9. The sound suggests a low lifeform like a(n) _____, slithering along the
   ground.

10. The tourist has a question about the "soft shapes," which are the _____
    inside the cars.

Southbound on the Freeway, page 543

Expository Writing

Choose a statement about the poem and write a paragraph in which you develop the ideas suggested by this topic sentence. Cite lines and phrases from the poem to support your position.

1. In contemporary society, humans are being overshadowed by machines and technology.

2. In this poem, Swenson sees the world through the lines and shapes of geometry.

3. "Southbound on the Freeway" is a riddle that the reader must figure out.

4. Swenson is both concrete and abstract at once.

5. Swenson uses humor to point out that humans have become too dependent on machines and technology.

6. The poem implies that observation without interaction leads to dangerous misconceptions.

_____

_____

_____

_____

_____

_____

_____

_____

_____

_____

_____

_____

_____

AFTER READING

Southbound on the Freeway, page 543

Selection Quiz

Multiple Choice

Write the letter of the correct answer on the line.

_____ 1. The "tourist" from Orbitville is really a(n)
    A. chauffeur.
    B. alien.
    C. teenager driver with a permit.

_____ 2. The speaker is
    A. an accurate observer.
    B. sent to conquer Earth.
    C. parked in the air over a freeway.

_____ 3. The "metal and glass" creatures are really
    A. cars.
    B. doors.
    C. robots.

_____ 4. The "round" feet are actually
    A. tires.
    B. donuts.
    C. rocks.

_____ 5. The front and rear lights are described as
    A. motion detectors.
    B. traffic signals.
    C. eyes.

_____ 6. The creature with "a red eye turning" is a(n)
    A. police car.
    B. ambulance.
    C. truck.

_____ 7. The poem ends with a
    A. moral.
    B. question.
    C. summary.

_____ 8. The speaker bases his observations on
    A. reports from Earth.
    B. rational, well-informed thought processes.
    C. sensory evidence (sight, sound, touch).

AFTER READING

Southern Mansion, page 548

Build Background: Antebellum South

Do online research to find the answers to the questions below.

1. When did the Antebellum period end?

   _____

2. What is the name of Margaret Mitchell's 1936 novel that romanticizes this period?

   _____

3. What was the name of the law that forced escaped slaves back to their masters in the South?

   _____

4. What agricultural products paid for the large southern mansions?

   _____

5. What is the name of a southern plantation that you can take a tour of?

   _____

6. Key "Antebellum Slavery PBS" and refer to the text on the official PBS Web site to answer the next questions. Were large plantations with hundreds of slaves common or rare?

   _____

7. How many slaves did the largest plantations have?

   _____

8. How did young children of both races interact?

   _____

9. What happened to black families on the auction block?

   _____

10. What was the underlying principal of the Slave Codes?

    _____

BEFORE READING

Build Background: Slave Narrative

A. Read a page of a slave account from the nineteenth century, for example, one by Frederick Douglas, Harriet Tubman, or Harriet Jacobs. Then summarize what you learned.

_____

_____

_____

_____

_____

_____

_____

_____

_____

B. If you were a slave who lived through the experiences described in Part A, how would you feel toward white people and their way of life? Write a short paragraph to answer this question.

_____

_____

_____

_____

_____

_____

_____

_____

_____

_____

Meeting the Standards   © EMC Publishing, LLC

BEFORE READING

Southern Mansion, page 548

Literary Connection: Literary Terms

A. Fill in the blank with the word from the box that best completes each sentence about the poem. You will use one word twice.

theme	setting	symbol	onomatopeia

1. A southern plantation home, its grounds, and the agricultural fields are the _____ for this poem.

2. To the poet, the mansion is a(n) _____ of the antebellum south.

3. The word "tinkling" in line 9 is an example of the sound device _____.

4. The "roses" in line 15 are a(n) _____ of the pre-Civil War era.

5. The ghosts of the black "bondmen" haven't forgotten; their retribution in line 15 is the

   _____ of the poem.

B. Circle the word or phrase that best describes the feature of the poem on the left-hand side. (For one item, you will need to circle both descriptors.)

6. Tone: quiet   noisy
7. Motif: city life   natural world
8. Mood: haunting   realistic
9. Time period: present   past
10. Compares and contrasts: dead and alive things   lives of slave
                                                          owners and slaves

Southern Mansion, page 548

Use Reading Strategies: Make Inferences

A. Make inferences by filling in the chart with answers to the questions on the left.

Parts of the Poem to Consider:	Inference:
1. Lines 1–5 Are the slave owners or the slaves being described? What words indicate this?	
2. Lines 6–10 How is music used in this stanza?	
3. Line 11 What does the "iron clank" indicate?	
4. Line 12 What does the gate symbolize?	
5. Line 13 What emotion does "trembles" evoke?	
6. Line 15 Who are the ghosts? How would you describe the retribution of the ghosts—harsh or mild?	
7. Line 16 What is the purpose of this line?	

B. Write a paragraph in which you explain the meaning of the poem. Refer to the chart you filled out in Part A for ideas.

_____

_____

_____

_____

_____

DURING READING

Meeting the Standards

Southern Mansion, page 548

Expository Writing

A. Turn the sentences below into topic sentences by circling the most logical
    word.

1. The poem "Southern Mansion" is about the (death, artifacts) of a way of life.

2. Bontemps' free verse is (emotional, restrained) throughout "Southern Mansion."

3. The theme of "Southern Mansion" is the (retribution, salvation) of the slave victims.

4. In "Southern Mansion," the poet takes a(n) (subjective, objective) view of the enslavement of his
    ancestors.

5. In "Southern Mansion," Bontemps shows a closeness to (nature, learning).

B. Select one of the topic sentences above and develop the idea in a paragraph.
    Cite examples from the poem to support your position.

_____

_____

_____

_____

_____

_____

_____

_____

_____

_____

_____

_____

_____

_____

_____

_____

_____

AFTER READING

Southern Mansion, page 548

Selection Quiz

Multiple Choice

Write the letter of the correct answer on the line.

_____ 1. There are two main settings in the poem, the southern mansion and the
A. fields where the slaves work.
B. rose garden.

_____ 2. The southern mansion is linked to the fields through the motif of
A. ghosts.
B. musical sounds.

_____ 3. The grand life in the southern mansion was paid for by selling
A. cotton.
B. rice.

_____ 4. "Poplars are standing there still as death" is an example of a
A. metaphor.
B. simile.

_____ 5. In "A dry leaf trembles on the wall," the verb "trembles" suggests
A. doubt about who's ruining the rose bushes.
B. fear due to the ghosts walking the property.

_____ 6. The tone of the poem is
A. somber.
B. light-hearted.

_____ 7. The inhabitants of the southern mansion enjoyed a life of
A. hard work in the fields.
B. wealth and leisure.

_____ 8. The poet is saying that
A. we should bring back the lifestyle of the people who lived in
southern mansions.
B. sins of the past aren't easily forgotten.

_____ 9. The poplars are
A. stable witnesses to events.
B. in the shade.

_____ 10. The chains of the "bondmen" symbolize
A. slavery.
B. prison.

Bats, page 551

Build Background: Myth or Fact?

A. Interview ten teens about their perceptions of bats. Ask each one an indicated
   question, or think of another question.

   - Do you associate bats with vampires?
   - Do you think bats are scary?
   - Do you think bats have a function in the ecosystem?
   - Do you think bats are flying rats?

Names:	Yes:	No:
1.		
2.		
3.		
4.		
5.		
6.		
7.		
8.		
9.		
10.		

Report on your findings to the class, for example: "I asked ten teens if they associate
bats with vampires. Six out of ten said yes. Consequently, 60% of teens think of
vampires when they think of bats."

B. Do online research about bats so you can fill in the chart with a check mark in
   the appropriate column. If the statement indicates a myth about bats, correct
   the misconception with a factual statement.

Statement:	Myth:	Fact:	Corrected Myths:
1. Bats are flying rats.			
2. Bats are birds with fur.			
3. Bats are unclean.			
4. Bats like to scare people.			
5. Bats are blind.			
6. Bats like to suck blood.			
7. Bats have no use in the ecosystem.			
8. If a person is near a bat, the bat will most likely get tangled in the person's hair.			

BEFORE READING

Bats, page 551

Use Reading Skills: Identify Author's Purpose

A writer's **purpose** is his or her aim, or goal. People usually write with one or more of the following purposes: to inform or explain; to portray a person, place, object, or event; to convince people to accept a position and respond in some way; to express thoughts or ideas; or to tell a story.

A. On the line in front of each number, write the letter of the correct description of the content of those lines of the poem.

_____ 1. Lines 1–5; 21; 34

_____ 2. Lines 9; 17–20

_____ 3. Lines 3–4; 34

_____ 4. Lines 28–34

_____ 5. Lines 10–16

A. nocturnal activities
B. life of a baby bat
C. how bats' echolocation works
D. how mother bats care for their young
E. how bats sleep

B. Based on what you know about Randall Jarrell, what do you think his purpose in writing "Bats" was? (More than one purpose is possible.) Write a short paragraph in which you explain and support your position.

_____

_____

_____

_____

_____

_____

_____

_____

_____

_____

_____

DURING READING

Bats, page 551

Poet's Attitude toward His Subject

A. Circle the word that best describes Jarrell's attitude toward bats in the poem.

1. informed   uninformed

2. objective   subjective

3. sympathetic   unsympathetic

4. dismissive   respectful

5. unimpressed   impressed

B. Write a paragraph in which you describe and explain Jarrell's attitude toward bats.

_____

_____

_____

_____

_____

_____

_____

_____

_____

_____

_____

_____

_____

_____

_____

_____

_____

DURING READING

Bats, page 551

Text-to-Text Connection

A. Fill in the chart with an explanation of how the poets think people see bats.

"Bats"	"The Bat:
1. Lines 23–25:	3. Lines 7–8:
2. Line 30:	4. Lines 9–10:

B. Write a paragraph in which you compare and contrast how the two poets think people see bats. Which description is more objective? Which is more subjective? How do you think the poets feel about bats? Be sure to support your position with examples from the poems.

_____

_____

_____

_____

_____

_____

_____

_____

_____

_____

_____

_____

AFTER READING

Bats, page 551

Selection Quiz

A. Make a check mark in the appropriate column to indicate if Jarrell discusses each item in his poem.

Bat Topics:	Yes:	No:
1. newborn bat		
2. eating and drinking		
3. mother bat		
4. nocturnal activities		
5. interaction with humans		
6. myths and superstitions		
7. how bats sleep		
8. echolocation		

B. True or False

Write *T* if the statement is true or *F* if the statement is false.

_____ 9. A newborn bat is furry.

_____ 10. The mother bat has no milk for her babies.

_____ 11. Bats see their food at night.

_____ 12. Bats hang upside-down by their toes.

_____ 13. Bats sleep in groups.

The Choice, page 557

Build Background: My Partner

A. Ask a relative and a friend their opinion about what kind of person your partner should be. Fill in the chart with each person's response.

Question	Relative	Friend
1. What profession should my partner have?		
2. What two words would best describe my partner's personality?		
3. What two things do I need most from a partner?		
4. What hobbies and past-times should my partner participate in?		
5. Will my partner prefer to live in the city or country?		
6. How will my partner originally get my attention?		
7. Will my partner make a lot of money or just get by?		
8. Will my partner first impress me with his or her head or heart?		
9. What would be the perfect date for me?		
10. Will my partner be like me or my opposite?		

The Choice, page 557

Dorothy Parker's Life

In 1994 a movie, *Mrs. Parker and the Vicious Circle*, was released about Dorothy Parker's life. Read several reviews about this film. Then answer the following questions about Dorothy Parker's life, based on what you read.

1. Was Dorothy Parker lucky or unlucky in love? _____

2. Does the movie focus on her life in the 1920s or 1940s? _____

3. Is the movie set primarily in New York or Hollywood? _____

4. Did Dorothy Parker make quotes or use other people's quotes? _____

5. Did she have a problem with drug addiction or alcohol? _____

6. Was she a journalist or a screenwriter? _____

7. Was she a joiner or a loner? _____

8. Was she a poet or a novelist? _____

9. Did she like to associate with luminaries or ordinary people? _____

10. Did she stand up to men or shrink from them? _____

11. Did she live a happy life or a sad life? _____

12. Was she professionally successful or unsuccessful? _____

B. Write a paragraph describing what you think your life partner will be like.

_____

_____

_____

_____

Vocabulary: Nuances

A. Of all the languages in the world, English has the most words. The *Oxford English Dictionary* lists about 500,000 of them, not including a further half million technical and scientific terms that were not included. This means that when we write and speak we have a lot of words to choose from to make our descriptions detailed and pointed. A **nuance** is a shading of meaning. This means there are sometimes very subtle distinctions between words, as in the pairs below. Explain why Parker uses the words that are not underlined below and why she does not use the underlined words in her poem.

1. Line 4: smoldering vs. <u>fuming</u>

_____

2. Line 5: lilting vs. <u>spirited</u>

_____

3. Line 9: lace vs. <u>satin</u>

_____

4. Line 10: glimmered vs. <u>flickered</u>

_____

5. Line 10: sheen vs. <u>luster</u>

_____

B. Fill in the blank with the word in parentheses that best completes each sentence.

6. The _____ of the fabric matched the girl's hair. (luster, sheen)

7. The poet's _____ words reminded the spectator of the dialogue he had grown up with in his home town in Ireland. (lilting, spirited)

8. The candle _____ in the window as the breeze came in through the screen. (glimmered, flickered)

9. The neckline was adorned with _____ made in Belgium; it had a pattern of flowers and petals. (satin, lace)

10. The _____ muffler of the diesel bus obstructed the view of the passengers getting on and off. (fuming, smoldering)

DURING READING

The Choice, page 557

Analyze Literature: Make Judgments

As you read, make judgments about "The Choice" by answering the following questions.

1. How would you describe the lover described as "he" who would have given the speaker "rolling lands,/Houses of marble, and billowing farms,/Pearls, to trickle between [her] hands/Smoldering rubies . . . "?

   _____

2. How would you describe the personality of the lover addressed as "you"?

   _____

3. Would you describe the speaker's relationship with the lover described as "you" as a head-over-heels romance, or as a romance that developed slowly over time? Which words support your position?

   _____

4. If lines 2–4 can be characterized as gifts of property and jewels, how would you characterize the gifts described in lines 9–12?

   _____

5. Who was in charge in the relationship described in lines 13–14? How can you tell?

   _____

6. Which line makes this a humorous poem? How does it contrast to the rest of the poem?

   _____

DURING READING

The Choice, page 557

Text-to-Text Connection

A. Read two more love poems by Dorothy Parker, "Love Song" and "Light of Love."
    Then, imagining you are the poet, fill out the yes/no love questionnaire below.

1. Do you fall in love slowly? _____

2. Does your lover have to be wealthy? _____

3. Do you like romantic men? _____

4. Are you affected by generous gifts? _____

5. Are you willing to take a back seat in a relationship? _____

6. Do you feel sad at the end of a relationship? _____

7. Are you attracted to strong men? _____

8. Are you attracted to bold men? _____

9. Are you attracted to men who are sad? _____

10. Do you like to be alone? _____

B. Write a short paragraph that identifies either "Love Song" or "Light of Love" as
    being the most similar to "The Choice."

    _____

    _____

    _____

    _____

    _____

    _____

    _____

    _____

    _____

    _____

    _____

AFTER READING

The Choice, page 557

Selection Quiz

A. True or False

Write *T* if the statement is true or *F* if the statement is false.

_____1. Dorothy Parker is considered witty.

_____2. She was a successful critic.

_____3. She was a novelist.

_____4. She was a screenwriter.

_____5. She lived in the nineteenth and twentieth centuries.

B. Multiple Choice

Write the letter of the correct answer on the line.

_____6. In "The Choice," the speaker makes a choice between two
        A. vacations.
        B. career paths.
        C. sweethearts.

_____7. The line that makes the poem humorous is
        A. "Somebody ought to examine my head!"
        B. "Horses to draw me, as fine as a queen."
        C. "Only a melody, happy and high"

_____8. The sweetheart described as "he" was
        A. passionate and bold.
        B. rich and generous.
        C. strong and impulsive.

_____9. The sweetheart described as "he" was able to give the speaker
everything but
        A. property, including clothing.
        B. jewels and transportation.
        C. passion.

_____10. The speaker addresses the other sweetheart using
        A. the second-person pronoun.
        B. terms of endearment.
        C. the first-person pronoun.

AFTER READING

Ode to My Socks, page 560

Deduction: What is an Ode?

Find the following odes online and print a copy of each.

"Ode to the Yard Sale" by Gary Soto
"Ode to the Confederate Dead" by Allen Tate
"Ode to the West Wind" by Percy Bysshe Shelley
"Ode to a Nightengale" by John Keats
"Ode on a Grecian Urn" by John Keats

Read each ode. Then answer these questions.

1. What can odes be about?

    _____

2. Do odes criticize or exalt?

    _____

3. Are odes reflective or superficial?

    _____

4. Write your own definition of what an ode is. Your definition should encompass all five of the odes in the list above. What do all odes do? Does the poet writing an ode have to adhere to a certain stanza form?

    _____

    _____

5. Look up a definition for "ode." Were you close in your definition? Is there anything you didn't notice about what an ode is that should have been included in your definition?

    _____

    _____

BEFORE READING

Name: _____   Date: _____

Ode to My Socks, page 560

Build Background: *Il Postino*

In 1994 a film, *Il Postino*, was released, in which Pablo Neruda was a fictional
character. Read some reviews of the film. Then, for each description of the film that
follows, write an explanation of how it relates to Neruda's real life. You will also need
to read a biography about Neruda in order to do this activity.

1. In *Il Postino*, Pablo Neruda is living on an island off the coast of southern Italy.

   _____

   _____

2. He befriends a simple, uneducated Italian man named Mario, who delivers his
   mail.

   _____

   _____

3. Mario says, "The whole world is a metaphor for something."

   _____

   _____

4. Mario wants to learn how to woo women with poetry.

   _____

   _____

5. In a community election, Mario decides to vote for the Communist candidate.

   _____

   _____

BEFORE READING

Ode to My Socks, page 560

Vocabulary from Spanish Words

Scan the original Spanish version of the poem until you find the words in the list below:

1. manos _____

2. pastora _____

3. modo _____

4. luminosos _____

5. impulso _____

Now go back and write what each word means in English on the lines above.

Write each English word from the box after the Spanish word it comes from. Many words in English came from Latin, via one of the Romance languages (Spanish, French, Italian, etc.).

illuminated	pastorale	impulse	pastoral	illumine	pastor	
manual	luminous	manufacture	illumination	manumission	impulsive	mode

6. manos: _____

7. pastora: _____

8. modo: _____

9. luminosos: _____

10. impulso: _____

DURING READING

Ode to My Socks, page 560

Use Reading Skills: Monitor Comprehension

Write the letter of the correct answer on the line.

_____ 1. Maru Mori is
   A. the name of a poem by Pablo Neruda.
   B. a person who lived in the country and made a pair of wool socks for
       the poet.

_____ 2. In the comparison "two socks as soft/as rabbits," the poet uses a
   A. simile.
   B. metaphor.

_____ 3. The poet uses the word "twilight" in line 15 because that is the hour
       when
   A. the sheepherder made the socks.
   B. ordinary objects become extraordinary due to the light.

_____ 4. Neruda feels he is _____ by the gift of the socks.
   A. spoiled
   B. honored

_____ 5. In lines 34–38, the poet compares his socks to _____ and finds the
       latter _____.
   A. firemen; aged
   B. his feet; defective

_____ 6. Neruda describes the socks as "woven fire" and "glowing" because
   A. the socks are warm and it's cold outside.
   B. they were sewn with golden thread.

_____ 7. Neruda reflects on
   A. how the woman made the socks.
   B. whether he should save the socks or wear them.

_____ 8. The poet ends his ode with a
   A. moral.
   B. resolution.

_____ 9. His gift is "doubly good"
   A. because he has two socks made of wool and it is winter.
   B. he can store the socks in his dresser sometimes and wear them at
       other times.

DURING READING

Ode to My Socks, page 560

Expository Writing

Choose one of the topics below and write a paragraph that answers the question(s) about "Ode to My Socks."

1. How does Neruda use figurative language in the poem? What is he comparing? How effective are his comparisons?

2. Read about the history of the ode online or in the library. Does Neruda's use of the ode follow traditional patterns or break new ground? If so, how?

3. Read the following words from Neruda's Nobel lecture: "During this long journey I found the necessary components for the making of the poem. There I received contributions from the earth and from the soul. And I believe that poetry is an action, ephemeral or solemn, in which there enter as equal partners solitude and solidarity, emotion and action, the nearness to oneself, the nearness to mankind and to the secret manifestations of nature. And no less strongly I think that all this is sustained—man and his shadow, man and his conduct, man and his poetry—by an ever wider sense of community, by an effort which will forever bring together the reality and the dreams in us because it is precisely in this way that poetry unites and mingles them." How does this quotation apply to what can be found in this poem? For example, you might consider one part of this quote, such as Neruda's concept of community, "emotion and action," or "manifestations of nature" in terms of how it relates to the poem.

4. Neruda has been called an "accessible" poet. What makes this poem accessible to the reader?

_____

_____

_____

_____

_____

_____

_____

_____

_____

_____

AFTER READING

Ode to My Socks, page 560

Selection Quiz

A. Fill in the Blank

Fill in the blank to complete the sentence.

1. Pablo Neruda lived in Asia when he was a(n) _____ representing his country.

2. He was born in the country of _____ .

3. He published his first poem when he was a(n) _____ .

4. He also served as a(n) _____ of his South American nation.

5. He won the _____ , a prestigious literary award, in 1971.

B. Multiple Choice

Write the letter of the correct answer on the line.

_____ 6. The speaker in "Ode to my Socks" can't decide whether to
     A. save or wear his new socks.
     B. go outside on a cold winter day.

_____ 7. The socks were made by
     A. the speaker's wife.
     B. a sheepherder.

_____ 8. The speaker doesn't compare his new socks to
     A. cannons.
     B. roosters.

_____ 9. In comparison to his beautiful new socks, the speaker thinks his
     A. sweater seems old and tattered.
     B. feet seem unworthy of such a gift.

_____ 10. The speaker ends his poem with a
     A. metaphor.
     B. moral.

AFTER READING

Casey at the Bat, page 566

Build Background: Baseball Quiz

A. Write ten baseball questions for your partner. Find out from him or her how much he or she knows about baseball. Then create a quiz that is easy, moderate, or difficult. In other words, the test should reflect his or her knowledge level. You may want to use an online baseball quiz to get ideas. Write your questions below.

1. _____

2. _____

3. _____

4. _____

5. _____

6. _____

7. _____

8. _____

9. _____

10. _____

B. Ask your partner the questions and have him or her write the answers on a separate sheet of paper.

C. Write a paragraph in which you describe what you learned about baseball by writing and giving the quiz.

_____

_____

_____

_____

_____

_____

_____

_____

BEFORE READING

Casey at the Bat, page 566

Literary Connection: Allusions

An **allusion** is a reference to a well-known person, event, object, or work from history or literature. In "Casey at the Bat," the speaker says, "The rest/Clung to the hope which springs eternal in the human breast . . . " This is an allusion to British poet and translator Alexander Pope, who said in a poem, "Hope springs eternal in the human breast."

A. Explain why you think Alexander Pope's line has been quoted so often.

_____

_____

_____

_____

B. Find online Abbot and Costello's comedy sketch about baseball by keying in "Who's on First." Print a copy of the sketch and read it or listen to it online. Then find an allusion to the sketch and describe it below.

Alluded to by: _____

When: _____

Purpose of the allusion: _____

_____

_____

Arena (comedy? baseball? politics? education? etc.): _____

_____

_____

_____

BEFORE READING

Casey at the Bat, page 566

Vocabulary: Synonyms

A. Poets and other writers don't reuse the same word over and over. They often use synonyms to vary their expression. Baseball is played with a bat and a _____. Write the three ways this noun is referred to in the poem.

1. Line 14: _____

2. Line 29: _____

3. Line 39: _____

B. As you read the poem, stop for a moment to write the letter of the correct synonym on the line next to the matching word or expression from the poem.

_____ 4. outlook

_____ 5. sickly

_____ 6. patrons

_____ 7. whack

_____ 8. fake

_____ 9. multitude

_____10. melancholy

_____11. wonderment

_____12. much-despised

_____13. joyous

_____14. applaud

_____ 15. shore

A. hated
B. crowd
C. depression, sadness
D. coast, beach
E. strike, hit
F. prospect
G. imposter
H. clap
I. ill
J. amazement
K. clients, customers
L. happy

DURING READING

Casey at the Bat, page 566

Literary Connection: Narrative Events

A **narrative poem** is verse that tells a story. There are events in a narrative poem.

A. Write the events from the story about the Mudville baseball team in the correct order on the lines below.

Casey doffs his hat.
Casey misses his first hit.
Cooney and Burrows don't get to stay on first base.
The Mudville crowd gets angry at the umpire.
Casey strikes out on his last hit.
There is no joy in Mudville.
Casey ignores the second pitch.
Blake is safe on second, and Flynn is safe on third.

1. _____

2. _____

3. _____

4. _____

5. _____

6. _____

7. _____

8. _____

B. On the lines below, indicate the number of the stanza in which each event occurs.

1. _____   5. _____

2. _____   6. _____

3. _____   7. _____

4. _____   8. _____

DURING READING

Casey at the Bat, page 566

Analyze Literature: Parody

A **parody** is a literary or musical work in which the style of an author or work is closely imitated for comic effect or ridicule. In 1994, radio host and writer Garrison Keillor wrote a parody of "Casey at the Bat" called "Casey at the Bat (Road Game)." Find Keillor's poem online and print a copy. Write a paragraph in which you describe how Keillor parodies the original "Casey at the Bat." For example, you might consider rhyme scheme, events, and characterization. Also indicate the point of view in Keillor's version and his use of humor to make fun of Thayer's poem.

_____

_____

_____

_____

_____

_____

_____

_____

_____

_____

_____

_____

_____

_____

_____

_____

_____

_____

_____

_____

_____

_____

_____

AFTER READING

Casey at the Bat, page 566

Selection Quiz

Multiple Choice

Write the letter of the correct answer on the line.

_____ 1. At the beginning of the game the Mudville fans feel
   A. worried and hopeful.
   B. tense and defeated.

_____ 2. Most of the Mudville fans don't give up because
   A. they are die-hard fans.
   B. Flynn and Blake bat well, and Casey is up next.

_____ 3. Casey is a _____ player.
   A. confident
   B. boastful

_____ 4. After the first pitch when Casey is at the plate, the multitude gets
   angry at the umpire. This is a(n) _____ reaction, considering Casey's
   performance.
   A. rational
   B. irrational

_____ 5. The "ease in Casey's manner" and his "haughty grandeur" indicate he is
   a type of
   A. hero.
   B. reviled player.

_____ 6. This poem builds _____ by suggesting that *if only* Casey can play, the
   game will be saved for Mudville.
   A. suspense
   B. characterization

_____ 7. "Casey at the Bat" is a poem with _____ meaning.
   A. superficial
   B. deep

AFTER READING

Paul Revere's Ride, page 571

Build Background: Colonial America

A. Visit the official site for "Colonial Williamsburg" online. Click on "Historic Area,"
"Multimedia," and "Slideshows." View the slideshows on these topics: Seasons,
Trades, Buildings, Miscellaneous. For each category, describe one of the slides.

Seasons

_____

_____

_____

_____

Trades

_____

_____

_____

_____

Buildings

_____

_____

_____

_____

Miscellaneous

_____

_____

_____

_____

B. Now spend half an hour exploring this site. Write a paragraph describing what
you learned about life in colonial America.

_____

_____

_____

_____

Paul Revere's Ride, page 571

Build Background: Revolutionary America in Fiction

A. You are about to read a famous poem about Paul Revere's ride to alert the colonists that the British were coming. Paul Revere appears as a minor character in two novels for young readers about this time period, *Johnny Tremain* and *April Morning*. Do online research so that you can fill in the chart below with details about the two books.

	Johnny Tremain	April Morning
1. author		
2. setting of novel		
3. name of protagonist		
4. age of protagonist		
5. conflict(s) of protagonist		
6. how it is a coming of age story		
7. how Paul Revere is used in novel		

B. If you had to do a book report on one of these books, which one would you choose? Write a paragraph in which you explain your decision. Use information from the chart in Part A in your paragraph as you explain your preference.

_____

_____

_____

_____

_____

_____

_____

_____

_____

_____

BEFORE READING

Paul Revere's Ride, page 571

Colonial Lexicons

The poem describes an event in colonial America, right before the Revolutionary War begins. Choose one of the categories below and write in the meanings of the listed words as you come across them in your reading. Then do online research to add the number of new words to your lexicon that are indicated. For example, you might key in "18th century ships" or "British man-of-war" if you choose the nautical lexicon or "colonial militias" or "British army Revolutionary War" if you choose the military lexicon.

A. Nautical Lexicon

    1. moorings: _____

    2. man-of-war: _____

    3. mast: _____

    4. spar: _____

    5. _____

    6. _____

    7. _____

    8. _____

    9. _____

B. Military Lexicon

    10. muster: _____

    11. barracks: _____

    12. grenadiers: _____

    13. encampment: _____

    14. sentinel: _____

    15. musket: _____

    16. red-coats: _____

    17. _____

    18. _____

DURING READING

Paul Revere's Ride, page 571

Analyze Literature: Characterization

A. Fill in the chart with examples from the poem that demonstrate the following character traits of Paul Revere, as he is described by Longfellow.

Character Traits:	Examples:
1. decisiveness	
2. fearlessness	
3. love and respect for animals	
4. patriotism	
5. dependability	

B. Write a paragraph in which you describe how Longfellow portrays Paul Revere, using examples from the chart you completed in Part A.

_____

_____

_____

_____

_____

_____

_____

_____

_____

_____

_____

_____

_____

DURING READING

Paul Revere's Ride, page 571

Text-to-Text Connection

A. Indicate in the chart how each topic is treated by the writer of the poem and the nonfiction selection.

Topic:	Longfellow:	Esther Forbes:
1. Somerset		
2. Paul Revere's comrades		
3. British soldiers		
4. Lexington and Concord		
5. symbolic place of Paul Revere in history		

B. Write a paragraph in which you describe how poets and nonfiction writers differ in their approaches, using "Paul Revere's Ride" and Forbes's account as examples.

_____

_____

_____

_____

_____

_____

_____

_____

_____

_____

_____

_____

_____

AFTER READING

Paul Revere's Ride, page 571

Selection Quiz

Multiple Choice

Write the letter of the correct answer on the line.

_____ 1. The protagonist in the poem is
   A. the man who signals Paul Revere.
   B. Paul Revere.

_____ 2. The rising action includes
   A. Paul Revere instructing his friend how to signal him in the church tower.
   B. the description of the Old North Church.

_____ 3. The climax occurs when Paul Revere
   A. arrives in Lexington.
   B. sees two lanterns in the church tower.

_____ 4. The resolution occurs when Paul Revere
   A. warns his countrymen that the British are coming.
   B. becomes a patriotic hero of the Revolutionary War.

_____ 5. The conflict in the poem is between
   A. the American colonists and the British.
   B. the American colonists and the French.

_____ 6. Paul Revere is characterized as
   A. independent and headstrong.
   B. bold and fearless.

_____ 7. The _____ of the poem is *aabbb*.
   A. meter
   B. rhyme scheme

_____ 8. "And the meeting-house windows, black and bare,/Gaze at him with a spectral glare . . . " This is an example of
   A. symbolism.
   B. personification.

_____ 9. (Continuation of the two lines above.) "As if they already stood aghast/ At the bloody work they would look upon" is an example of
   A. foreshadowing.
   B. conflict.

AFTER READING

Grandma Ling, page 582

Build Background: Family Resemblances

In the poem "Grandma Ling," the speaker describes how she resembles her Chinese grandmother. In "My Mother Juggling Bean Bags," the speaker talks about a personality trait he would like to develop that his mother had. Indicate below the physical resemblances, personality traits, and behaviors people say you share with your parents or guardians.

Mom

1. _____
2. _____
3. _____
4. _____
5. _____

Dad

6. _____
7. _____
8. _____
9. _____
10. _____

Another relative: My _____

11. _____
12. _____
13. _____
14. _____
15. _____

Grandma Ling, page 582

Vocabulary: Compound Adjectives

In "Grandma Ling," the speaker describes the door of her Chinese grandmother's house as "paper-covered." In "My Mother Juggling Bean Bags," the speaker describes his Christmases as a child as "one-present Christmases." The poets use modifiers formed by combining two words; these are called compound adjectives. In these two instances, the two words are separated by a hyphen. Some compound adjectives are not hyphenated, such as *worldwide* and *halfhearted*.

A. Fill in the blank with the word from the box that best describes each noun.

densely-populated	old-fashioned	long-winded	tight-fisted
joke-filled	four-door	deep-sea	sure-footed
dimly-lit	good-looking		

1. _____ parties

2. _____ urban center

3. _____ miser

4. _____ Christmas

5. _____ runner

6. _____ basement

7. _____ orator

8. _____ model

9. _____ fishing

10. _____ sedan

B. Write five original sentences that use compound adjectives without hyphens.

11. _____

12. _____

13. _____

14. _____

15. _____

BEFORE READING

Grandma Ling, page 582

Use Reading Skills: Draw Conclusions

As you read the poem "Grandma Ling," draw conclusions by answering the questions and indicate how you arrived at each conclusion.

1. (Lines 1–3) Was the speaker a Chinese or American child when she was told to dig a hole to China?

   _____

2. (Lines 3–6) Was the speaker interested in her Chinese roots?

   _____

3. (Lines 3–6) How old was the speaker when she made her trip?

   _____

4. (Lines 3–6) Where do you think the speaker went?

   _____

5. (Lines 7–10) With which sense was the speaker first aware of her grandmother's presence?

   _____

6. (Lines 10–11) Which details indicate the grandmother's house is not an American house?

   _____

7. (Lines 12–14) Does the speaker share personality traits, behaviors, or a physical resemblance with her grandmother?

   _____

8. (Line 16) What does this line mean?

   _____

9. (Lines 17–19) For how long has the grandmother been separated from her son, the speaker's father?

   _____

10. (Line 22) What does the speaker show her grandmother by hugging her?

    _____

Meeting the Standards   © EMC Publishing, LLC

DURING READING

Grandma Ling, page 582

Use Reading Strategies: Ask Questions

Imagine you are the speaker and are about to meet your Chinese grandmother for the first time. Write a list of questions to ask her.

1. _____

2. _____

3. _____

4. _____

5. _____

6. _____

7. _____

8. _____

DURING READING

Text-to-Text Connection

A. Fill in the chart with an explanation of the legacy the old women give the speakers in both poems. Also indicate how the speakers show love and respect for the grandmother and mother, respectively, in the two poems.

	"Grandmother Ling"	**"My Mother Juggling . . ."**
1. legacy		
2. love and respect		

B. Write a short paragraph in which you explain how you would react if you met a relative for the first time who looked like you, like the speaker in "Grandma Ling" experiences with her Chinese grandmother. Also tell how you would react to a mother who was a joker, juggler, and prankster, like the speaker in "My Mother Juggling Bean Bags."

_____

_____

_____

_____

_____

_____

_____

_____

_____

_____

_____

AFTER READING

Grandma Ling, page 582

Selection Quiz

Multiple Choice

Write the letter of the correct answer on the line.

_____   1. The speaker lives in
A. China.
B. the United States.

_____   2. Where did the speaker have to go to see her grandmother?
A. Taiwan
B. Beijing

_____   3. How does the grandmother receive her granddaughter?
A. with reserve
B. with open arms

_____   4. The speaker shares _____ with her grandmother.
A. a physical resemblance
B. personality traits

_____   5. When did the grandmother's son leave China?
A. four years ago
B. twenty-five years ago

_____   6. What challenge did the grandmother and granddaughter share?
A. They couldn't communicate with each other in words.
B. They had to decide if the grandmother would move to the United States.

_____   7. The "aqua paper-covered door" and "tatami floor" indicate
A. the grandmother's house is in a foreign location.
B. the grandmother was concerned with appearances.

_____   8. When the speaker says, "my image stood before me,/acted on by fifty years," the speaker is imagining
A. what her grandmother looked like when she was young.
B. what she will look like when she's old.

_____   9. The speaker shows her grandmother love and respect by
A. hugging her.
B. giving her an American present.

AFTER READING

Exile, page 587

Build Background: A Place I Didn't Want to Leave

A. Draw a sketch of a place you didn't want to leave. Imagine that you are there
   seeing it once again. Carefully pick the perspective you want to show.

B. Above you showed what your special place looked like. Now write a description
   telling what you could hear, taste, touch, and smell when you were there.

_____

_____

_____

_____

_____

_____

_____

_____

BEFORE READING

Exile, page 587

Build Background: Claim Memories

In her creative nonfiction book *Silent Dancing*, Ortiz discusses the subjective nature of memory and the importance of claiming memories to make them your own.

A. Make a list of strong memories you have from the past month, year, or from your entire life.

1. _____

2. _____

3. _____

4. _____

5. _____

6. _____

7. _____

8. _____

B. Write four images about one of your memories.

_____

_____

_____

_____

C. On a separate sheet of paper, put the images in a logical order and add transitions between them. You have just written a poem. Congratulations!

BEFORE READING

Exile, page 587

Analyze Literature: Allusions

In lines 6–8, the poet makes a biblical allusion. An **allusion** is a reference to a well-known person, event, object, or work from history or literature. The Bible has provided writers with many allusions over the centuries.

A. Look up Genesis 19:15–26 in an online Bible. Read the story. Then write a summary that describes what warning was given, what Lot's wife did, and what happened to her.

_____

_____

_____

B. In what ways does the Bible passage relate to Cofer's poem "Exile"?

_____

_____

_____

C. In what ways does the Bible passage *not* relate to Cofer's poem?

_____

_____

_____

D. In what way do you think the poet intended the biblical allusion to Genesis 19 to be understood in her poem?

_____

_____

_____

DURING READING

Exile, page 587

Use Reading Strategies: Make Inferences

Read about Judith Ortiz Cofer's childhood and the themes of her writings online.
Then make inferences as you read the poem to answer the questions below.

1. Where is the home that Cofer refers to in line 1?

   _____

2. What does the poet mean to convey with the simile of the "cancelled postage stamp"?

   _____

3. In what way is Cofer like Lot's wife? (lines 6–11)

   _____

4. What does Cofer associate with the house where she was brought up? (lines 10–11)

   _____

5. What information does the image give about the speaker? (lines 12–17)

   _____

6. Did Cofer see continuity or change in her future? (lines 12–17)

   _____

7. What does the speaker want? (lines 8–11, 17–21)

   _____

8. What is the speaker willing to give up in order to get what she wants? (lines 8–9, 17–18)

   _____

9. Is she speaking literally or figuratively? (lines 8–9, 17–18)

   _____

10. How would you describe Cofer's memory of the fishermen? Why is this? (lines 17–21)

    _____

11. What do *skeletons, bled,* and *Hiroshima* reveal about her birthplace today? (lines 22–27)

    _____

12. What does this poem suggest about Cofer's back and forth movement between her two cultures
    when she was growing up?

    _____

DURING READING

Exile, page 587

Text-to-Text Connection

A. In both "Exile" and "Southern Mansion" (page 549) the speakers look back to
    the past. Fill in the chart to show how the two poems are alike and different.

	"Exile"	"Southern Mansion"
1. What type of poem is this?		
2. Where is the special place?		
3. What senses bring the past back?		
4. How would you categorize the images used?		
5. What was the past like?		
6. What is the role of the speaker?		
7. Why must the speakers remember these places?		

B. Write a paragraph in which you compare and contrast the two poems. Refer to
    the chart you filled out in Part A for ideas.

_____

_____

_____

_____

_____

_____

_____

AFTER READING

Exile, page 587

Selection Quiz

Multiple Choice

Write the letter of the correct answer on the line.

_____ 1. The speaker remembers her birthplace, a _____ area.
    A. coastal
    B. landlocked

_____ 2. When she looks back, she can see the _____ in the windows of her home.
    A. reflections of the palm trees
    B. faces of her family members

_____ 3. The danger of looking back is that
    A. her birthplace is no longer the same.
    B. it brings up bad memories.

_____ 4. The speaker is willing to _____ in order to see her home and the fishermen again.
    A. take a long trip
    B. sacrifice

_____ 5. The speaker used to go to the _____ with her friends and _____.
    A. plaza; dream of the future
    B. beach; watch the fishermen

_____ 6. Her memory of the shore is
    A. golden.
    B. insubstantial.

_____ 7. The _____ of houses remain in the town where the speaker used to live.
    A. foundations
    B. skeletons

_____ 8. The poem is called "Exile" because the speaker had to _____ her birthplace.
    A. stay too long in
    B. move from

AFTER READING

Birdfoot's Grampa / The Time We Climbed Snake Mountain, page 590

Build Background

Have you ever encountered animals in their natural habitat? What was your experience? Write your response on a separate sheet of paper.

Set Purpose

Preview the poems' titles and illustrations. Record your observations in the chart. Then write predictions about each poem's theme.

	"Birdfoot's Grampa"	"The Time We Climbed Snake Mountain"
What Title Suggests		
What Illustrations Suggest		
Possible Theme(s)		

Practice Vocabulary

Each sentence has two words that appear identical but have very different meanings.
Write the meaning of each underlined word in the sentence.

1. On our walk in the woods we (a) <u>spotted</u> a (b) <u>spotted</u> fawn.

   A. _____

   B. _____

2. That was a real (a) <u>live</u> snake; I think it must (b) <u>live</u> in these rocks.

   A. _____

   B. _____

3. We <u>climbed</u> into the truck wearily after we <u>climbed</u> the mountain.

   A. _____

   B. _____

4. We put out bird seed in several <u>places</u>; Handy Andy's Supply is the <u>place</u> we buy
   seed.

   A. _____

   B. _____

Birdfoot's Grampa / The Time We Climbed Snake Mountain, page 590

Compare Literature: Symbolism

A **symbol** is a thing that stands for or represents both itself and something else. Some traditional symbols include doves for peace, roads or paths for journeys through life, and owls for wisdom. As you read the two poems in this selection, think about what the images and actions might represent. How might the symbolism add to the meaning of the poems?

Write images and actions that you think are significant in the chart below. Then list ideas or concepts you associate with each image or action.

Images/Actions	Associations
"Birdfoot's Grampa" 1. 2. 3. 4.	
"The Time We Climbed Snake Mountain" 5. 6. 7. 8.	

Birdfoot's Grampa / The Time We Climbed Snake Mountain, page 590

Compare Literature: Symbolism (continued)

Both "Birdfoot's Grampa" and "The Time We Climbed Snake Mountain" describe
specific events. At the same time, the events, the people, and the objects in the poem
represent something other than themselves. This symbolism gives the poems larger
meanings. To analyze the symbolism in these poems, complete the chart below.
Then use it to answer the questions that follow.

"Birdfoot's Grampa"

Symbol	Details	What It Suggests
car	gives out a blinding light	It suggests the dangers of human technologies on the natural world.

"The Time We Climbed Snake Mountain"

Symbol	Details	What It Suggests
mountain	has "warm parts"	The mountain is a living place.

1. What are the themes of the poems? _____

_____

_____

_____

_____

2. How are the symbols in the two poems related? _____

_____

_____

_____

_____

_____

AFTER READING

Birdfoot's Grampa / The Time We Climbed Snake Mountain, page 590

Compare Literature: Imagery

Specific, concrete details appeal to the senses and create **images** inside the reader's mind. Identify imagery in "Birdfoot's Grampa" and "The Time We Climbed Snake Mountain" in the chart below. Then complete the chart by describing the effect of this imagery.

	"Birdfoot's Grampa"	**"The Time We Climbed Snake Mountain"**
Imagery	1. 2. 3.	8. 9. 10.
Effect of Imagery	4. 5. 6. 7.	11. 12. 13. 14.

Write a paragraph to compare and contrast the imagery from these two poems. Use the information from your chart in your answer.

_____

_____

_____

_____

_____

_____

_____

_____

_____

AFTER READING

Birdfoot's Grampa / The Time We Climbed Snake Mountain, page 590

Use Reading Strategies: Make Connections

Read each connection. Write your response on the lines below.

Text-to-Text   Compare the grandfathers in "Birdfoot's Grampa" and "The Medicine Bag" from Unit 2 (pages 211–219). How are these two characters similar? How are they different? Compare the attitude of the speaker or narrator toward the grandfather in each selection.

_____

_____

_____

_____

_____

Text-to-Self   Think about a time when you encountered a wild creature in nature. What did you feel? How did you act? Why do you think you had this reaction?

_____

_____

_____

_____

_____

Text-to-World   Think about what is happening to wild, natural places around the world. What conflict exists between nature and civilization? How do you think this conflict can be resolved?

_____

_____

_____

_____

_____

AFTER READING

Birdfoot's Grampa / The Time We Climbed Snake Mountain, page 590

Focus on "Birdfoot's Grampa"

Mirrors & Windows Question

Would you have acted the same way the grandfather does in the poem? Why might it be important to protect other forms of life, such as animals? Explain your answers on a separate sheet of paper.

Selection Quiz

Literary Element   Write *image* or *figure of speech* to identify each example of a poetic element.

_____   1.   "gather into his hands the small toads"

_____   2.   "live drops of rain"

_____   3.   "leathery hands full of wet brown life"

_____   4.   "knee deep in summer roadside grass"

In a Few Words   Answer each question with a word or phrase.

5.   In what are Birdfoot and the old man traveling? _____

_____

6.   What are the toads doing? _____

_____

7.   Why does the old man get out again and again? _____

_____

8.   What does the speaker in the poem want the grandfather to do? _____

_____

9.   Why is it important that the poem's setting is a roadway? _____

_____

10.   How does the old man feel about the lives of the toads? _____

_____

AFTER READING

Birdfoot's Grampa / The Time We Climbed Snake Mountain, page 590

Focus on "The Time We Climbed Snake Mountain"

Mirrors & Windows Question

Are you concerned about animals and their habitats? What is being done to protect animals in the wild? What else might be done to ensure their survival? Explain your answers on a separate sheet of paper.

Selection Quiz

Naming   Write the person or place from the poem beside the action it performs.

the speaker	mountain	snake

_____   1. grabs for hand holds

_____   2. sleeps on a rock

_____   3. asks climbers not to step on the snake

_____   4. belongs to snake

_____   5. offers warmth

Multiple Choice   Write the letter of the correct answer on the line.

_____   6. The speaker is most concerned with whose life or lives?
A. the mountain   C. the snake
B. the climbers   D. the speaker

_____   7. Details in the poem suggest what about the weather?
A. sunny and hot
B. stormy
C. cool and overcast
D. hot but threatening rain

_____   8. Who is the speaker most likely addressing?
A. other snakes
B. the speaker's family
C. people the speaker wants to educate
D. people the speaker does not like

_____   9. Which of the following BEST characterizes the speaker's relationship to the snake?
A. angry
B. respectful
C. close and personal
D. symbolic

_____   10. Which of the following BEST describes the speaker's attitude toward the mountain?
A. fearful
B. unfamiliar
C. detached and indifferent
D. reverent

AFTER READING

Birdfoot's Grampa / The Time We Climbed Snake Mountain, page 590

What Do You Think?

You have compared the use of symbolism in "Birdfoot's Grampa" and "The Time We Climbed Snake Mountain." Now compare your thoughts and feelings about the poems themselves.

    Which poem do you like better? Why? In the chart below, write your opinion and at least three strong, convincing reasons that support your opinion.

Opinion
I like the poem "_____" better than the poem
"_____."
Reasons
1 _____
2 _____
3 _____

Use the chart to write a paragraph in which you state your opinion and support it with your reasons.

_____

_____

_____

_____

_____

_____

_____

_____

_____

_____

_____

AFTER READING

The Cremation of Sam McGee, page 594

Practice Vocabulary

Write the correct word from the box to complete each sentence. Use the line number in parentheses to find the word in the poem and look for context clues to meaning. If necessary, consult a dictionary.

boiler (45)	brawn (31)	code (33)	derelict (41)	grisly (53)
marge (7)	moil (2)	mushing (13)	planks (45)	remains (24)

1. Flexing his muscles, the prize fighter showed off his _____.

2. Graceful cattails stood on the _____ of the pond.

3. Among people of all societies, there is a _____ of honor.

4. When our goldfish died, we buried the _____ in the yard.

5. After the earthquake, rescuers found a _____ scene of destruction.

6. Divers found a _____ that had once powered the mighty ship, now a wreck, with its heat.

7. Over and over again, the prospectors would stake a claim and _____ for gold.

8. A prospector and his dog team went _____ along the ice and snow.

9. The boat we found on the beach was a sun-bleached _____ with warped, rotting sides.

10. To repair the cabin floor, they cut rough _____ from logs and sanded them smooth.

DURING OR AFTER READING

The Cremation of Sam McGee, page 594

Analyze Literature: Narrative Poetry

A narrative poem is a story in verse form. It has a plot that is introduced, builds to a climax, and is resolved. Use the diagram below to trace the plot of "The Cremation of Sam McGee."

Climax

Rising Action   Falling Action

Plot Diagram

Exposition   Resolution

1. **Exposition:** _____

   _____

   _____

2. **Rising Action:** _____

   _____

   _____

3. **Climax:** _____

   _____

   _____

4. **Falling Action:** _____

   _____

   _____

5. **Resolution:** _____

   _____

   _____

Meeting the Standards

DURING READING

The Cremation of Sam McGee, page 594

Analyze Literature: Meter

The **meter** of "The Cremation of Sam McGee" is predictable and regular. Scan the lines from the poem by marking ˘ above each unstressed syllable and / above each stressed syllable. Mark | between each metric foot. An example has been provided for you.

˘ ˘ / ˘ /   ˘ ˘ /   ˘   /   ˘ ˘   /   ˘ /   ˘   /

 And that ver|y night, | as we lay | packed tight | in our robes | beneath | the snow,

Scan the following lines.

Now a promise made is a debt unpaid, and the trail has its own stern code.

In the days to come, though my lips were dumb, in my heart how I cursed that load.

Answer the questions below to analyze the meter of "The Cremation of Sam McGee."

1. How many feet are found in each line of the poem?

   _____

2. What is the pattern of unstressed and stressed syllables?

   _____

   _____

3. Read the lines on this page aloud, using the marks as a guide to expression. Explain how the meter affects the mood and meaning of the poem.

   _____

   _____

   _____

   _____

   _____

   _____

   _____

   _____

The Cremation of Sam McGee, page 594

Selection Quiz

What Happened Where   Write each place next to the event that happened there.

Plumtree, Tennessee	Lake Lebarge	Dawson trail	the Alice May

1. _____: where Sam McGee is cremated

2. _____: where derelict is discovered

3. _____: where Sam grew up

4. _____: where Sam died

About the Poetic Elements   Write a brief answer to each question.

5. Where is end rhyme used? _____

6. Where is internal rhyme used? _____

7. In the excerpt "the huskies, round in a ring,/Howled out their woes to the homeless snows," the underlined letters illustrate what two sound devices?

_____

8. The phrase "it [the cold] stabbed like a driven nail" illustrates what type of

figurative language? _____

Multiple Choice   Write the letter of the correct answer on the line.

_____ 9. What is the profession of the characters in the poem?
   A. soldiers
   B. prospectors
   C. outlaws
   D. sailors

_____ 10. Why is the speaker in the poem determined to cremate Sam?
   A. Sam owed him money.
   B. He was angry with Sam.
   C. He promised Sam he would.
   D. It is the right thing to do.

_____ 11. In the line "And every day that quiet clay seemed to heavy and heavier grow," what is the clay?
   A. Sam's body
   B. a pack of food
   C. gold dust
   D. the speaker's conscience

_____ 12. What about the crematorium does the speaker find astonishing?
   A. It is well designed.
   C. It is from Tennessee.
   B. It doesn't function.
   D. It revives Sam.

AFTER READING

The Cremation of Sam McGee, page 594

Describe and Critique: Poetry

Describe the poem "The Cremation of Sam McGee." Write the information to fill in these charts.

Title _____
Author _____
Type of Poem _____
Poetic Form
_____
Handling of Line and Stanza
Line: _____
_____
Stanza: _____
_____
How Form Affects Meaning _____
_____
_____
Use of Figurative Language, Imagery, Sound Effects
1. _____
2. _____
3. _____
4. _____
Effect on Mood and Meaning: _____
_____
Summary of Poem's Meaning
_____
_____
_____

AFTER READING

Critique, or review and evaluate, the poem "The Cremation of Sam McGee."
Answer these questions.

What do you think of the poem's format? (Are line and stanza skillfully handled? Does its appearance suit its message? Is its organizational plan appropriate?)

_____

_____

_____

What do you think of the poet's use of imagery, figurative language, and sound effects? (Are images clear and compelling? Are metaphors, similes, and personifications vivid and worthwhile? How do rhythm and rhyme or other sound devices enhance meaning?)

_____

_____

_____

What is your opinion of the poem? (What do you like about it? Why? What do you dislike about it? Why?)

_____

_____

_____

Give reasons for your opinion. Support them with examples and details from the poem.

_____

_____

_____

Would you recommend the poem to others? Why or why not?

_____

_____

_____

AFTER READING

Nikki-Rosa, page 598

Practice Vocabulary

The underlined words are words with multiple meanings. For each sentence, circle the correct meaning of the underlined word.

1. Losing the key to the house during the snowstorm was a <u>drag</u>.
   to pull along / a thing used to haul heavy items / a thing that ruins enjoyment

2. Climbing Mt. Kilimanjaro has always been a <u>dream</u> of mine.
   strongly desired goal / series of images during sleep / creation of the imagination

3. The peasants in the mountains had a <u>hard</u> life, but they seemed happy.
   resentful / difficult / rigid and tough

4. Every August my aunt and uncle <u>barbecue</u> a whole hog in the backyard.
   a social gathering / to roast over a heat source / a large animal roasted whole

5. She set aside money out of every paycheck to buy some <u>stock</u> or a bond.
   a supply kept for use or sale / broth for making soup / shares of a corporation

6. Her parents <u>attended</u> the open house at school and talked to her teachers.
   applied oneself / cared for / were present at

7. Dirty laundry was soaked, washed, and rinsed in aluminum <u>tubs</u> on the back steps.
   multipurpose container of wood or metal / a bathtub / to wash or place in a tub

8. The old woman had many fond <u>remembrances</u> of evenings spent with family on the porch.
   greetings / memories / memorials

Nikki-Rosa, page 598

During Reading Questions

Answer these questions while you are reading "Nikki-Rosa."

Title   **Use Reading Strategies: Make Predictions**   Who do you think this poem is about? What could be the meaning behind the name "Nikki-Rosa"? _____

_____

_____

Line 6   **Use Reading Skills: Draw Conclusions**   Who are "they"? How does the speaker feel about *them*? _____

_____

_____

Lines 9–11   **Analyze Literature: Imagery**   How do you picture the speaker's childhood home? What feeling about home does this image create? _____

_____

_____

Lines 18–19   **Use Reading Strategies: Evaluate Cause and Effect**   What has happened here? What might have caused this to happen? _____

_____

_____

Lines 29–30   **Analyze Literature: Theme**   What is the speaker saying? How does this idea relate to her values? _____

_____

_____

DURING READING

Nikki-Rosa, page 598

Analyze Literature: Speaker and Meaning

The meaning of a poem in some ways depends on the speaker. The speaker's attitude colors everything that is said and controls what readers and listeners understand about the subject. Record details about the speaker in "Nikki-Rosa" and her attitude in the first column. In the main idea box, write a conclusion about this person based on details from the first column.

Details
        Main Idea

	→
	→
	→
	→

Explain how the conclusion helps you understand the meaning of the poem.

_____

_____

_____

_____

_____

_____

Meeting the Standards

AFTER READING

Nikki-Rosa, page 598

Use Reading Strategies: Make Connections

Text-to-Text   How do "Nikki-Rosa" and "The Cremation of Sam McGee" differ in their use of imagery, figurative language, and sound effects? Explain how this difference is related to each poet's purpose.

_____

_____

_____

_____

_____

_____

_____

_____

_____

Text-to-Self   How do you define wealth? What would make you consider yourself wealthy? How are happiness and wealth related, in your opinion? In your answer, give examples from your experiences.

_____

_____

_____

_____

_____

_____

_____

_____

_____

AFTER READING

Nikki-Rosa, page 598

Describe and Critique: Poetry

Describe the poem "Nikki-Rosa." Write the information to fill in these charts.

Title _____	
Author _____	
Type of Poem _____	

Poetic Form

_____

Handling of Line and Stanza

Line: _____

_____

Stanza: _____

_____

How Form Affects Meaning _____

_____

_____

Use of Figurative Language, Imagery, Sound Effects

1. _____

2. _____

3. _____

4. _____

Effect on Mood and Meaning: _____

_____

Summary of Poem's Meaning

_____

_____

_____

AFTER READING

Critique, or review and evaluate, the poem "Nikki-Rosa." Answer these questions.

What do you think of the poem's format? (Are line and stanza skillfully handled? Does its appearance suit its message? Is its organizational plan appropriate?)

_____

_____

_____

What do you think of the poet's use of imagery, figurative language, and sound effects? (Are images clear and compelling? Are metaphors, similes, and personifications vivid and worthwhile? How do rhythm and rhyme or other sound devices enhance meaning?)

_____

_____

_____

What is your opinion of the poem? (What do you like about it? Why? What do you dislike about it? Why?)

_____

_____

_____

Give reasons for your opinion. Support them with examples and details from the poem.

_____

_____

_____

Would you recommend the poem to others? Why or why not?

_____

_____

_____

AFTER READING

ANSWER KEY

Poetry Study Guide

Understanding Meaning in Poetry

What elements do poets use to give *meaning* to poems? figurative language, sound devices, imagery

Why is the *meaning* of a poem often challenging to understand? Poems look at people, things, or events in unusual, imaginative ways and do not use language literally.

Narrator

What is it? storyteller; describing voice
Where is it found? inside the story as a character or outside the story as an observer
Describe the point of view. Are events seen from inside or outside the action? If the narrator is a character, the events are experienced inside the action. If the story has a third-person narrator, events are seen from outside the action.

Speaker

What is it? the voice that tells the poem
Where is it found? inside the story as a character or outside the story as an observer
Describe the point of view. Is the speaker's voice the same as the poet's voice? The speaker might be a fictional character, animal, or even an object or idea. Therefore, the speaker is not always the poet.

How are *narrator* and *speaker* similar? How are they different? Explain your answer. The narrator of a story is the voice that tells the story. In a poem, this voice is called the speaker. Like a narrator, a speaker can speak from inside the poem (as a character) or outside it (as an observer). Unlike a narrator, a speaker can be an object or idea. A story's narrator is almost always a person.

What is a *symbol*? A symbol is a thing that stands for itself and something else—often an idea or principle.

What do the following traditional *symbols* represent?
roses love   **doves** peace
roads journeys   **owls** wisdom

What does it mean to describe a *symbol* as "subjective"? When symbols are described as "subjective," it means that they are personal, not universal. An object may have completely different symbolic meanings in different poems or contexts.

Applying Meaning in Poetry to the Selections

"Birdfoot's Grampa" impatient, bossy
Both Possible answer: the speakers' interactions with animals show how they feel about nature
"Snake Mountain" mellow, appreciates nature

Reread "Bats" on page 552 in your text. Consider the descriptions of the mother bat and the baby bat. Summarize the feelings or beliefs about bats that the poet wants to express. Possible answer: The poet stresses the helplessness of the baby and the protective instinct of the mother. The adult bat soars, loops, catches her food, and even drinks while flying. The poet seems to want readers to admire these strange but gifted creatures.

What is the *meaning* of the following lines from "Bats"? How do the lines differ from the prose explanation of echolocation on page 553? Bats bounce sound waves off objects to hunt and navigate. The poem emphasizes the precision of this process though sensory details and the image of needlepoints. These images add a sharp, urgent mood that the prose lacks. They are also more imaginative.

Symbol **Somerset, a British man-of-war (ship)**
Represents British oppression of the colonists
Qualities/Characteristics dark, ghostly, hulking, suggests prison
What It Adds to Meaning/Mood foreboding, danger

Symbol **tower of Old North Church**
Represents watchfulness of the revolutionaries
Qualities/Characteristics lonely, somber, still
What It Adds to Meaning/Mood hushed anticipation, strength

Symbol **spark struck by Revere's steed**
Represents spirit of revolt
Qualities/Characteristics flash in the dark; heat; kindles the flame of revolt in the land
What It Adds to Meaning/Mood inspiration; fire for freedom; fearlessness

Symbol **bridge in Concord town**
Represents point of decision, no return; place to take a stand
Qualities/Characteristics site of bloodshed, loss of life
What It Adds to Meaning/Mood commitment, sorrow, sacrifice

Symbol **Revere's cry of alarm**
Represents statement of intent to fight for liberty
Qualities/Characteristics defiant, echoing
What It Adds to Meaning/Mood courageous spirit

Summarize the *meaning* of "The Time We Climbed Snake Mountain." Explain how the poet involved your imagination in communicating this meaning.
Possible answer: The poem's speaker pleads for people to respect the natural world and its residents, as they were there before us and have first claim to it. The poet used warm images and phrases like "I feel the mountain" to help readers imagine the scene and understand the mountain as a character.

Reviewing Imagery and Figurative Language

A poet creates imaginative word pictures by including imagery in his or her poem.

Figurative language **differs from literal language in that it is understood with the imagination.**

1. personification; Possible answer: the popcorn danced cheerfully
2. metaphor; Possible answer: his hand is a weathered road map
3. hyperbole; Possible answer: a howl louder than thunder
4. imagery; Possible answer: patterns of lacy frost on the cold grass
5. simile; Possible answer: her character is solid as granite

Applying Imagery and Figurative Language to the Selections

Stanza 2 Possible answer:
Image 1 music echoing through the open door
Sense(s) It Involves sound

Stanza 2 Possible answer:
Image 2 chains of bondmen dragging, tinkling
Sense(s) It Involves sound, touch

Stanza 3 Possible answer:
Image 1 a hand on a clanking iron gate
Sense(s) It Involves sight, sound

Stanza 3 Possible answer:
Image 1 a dry leaf trembling on a wall
Sense(s) It Involves sight, touch

In "The Choice," what qualities of the rejected suitor are emphasized by the *images*? The speaker emphasizes which qualities of the man she chose?
The rejected suitor is wealthy and generous; the man she chose sings well and is "sudden and swift and strong."

In "Ode to My Socks," list four adjectives the poet uses to describe the socks. Explain what each adjective emphasizes. Tell how each changes the *image* of the socks.
Possible answers:

1. violent: shocking, probably because their color is vivid; they have an unexpected quality that brings the speaker's senses to life
2. heavenly: beautiful and desirable, probably because of their softness and warmth; they make the speaker very happy
3. glowing: warm and warming to his heart; they bring gratitude and affection into his life
4. magnificent: uniqueness, superiority, excellence; feeling unworthy, the speaker puts on the socks, symbol of beauty and goodness

Reread stanza 6 of "Casey at the Bat." What do the images in this stanza add to your understanding of Casey's character?
The images reveal Casey to be proud and comfortable with his athletic skill and the crowd's adoration. He agrees with the crowd that he is "the greatest."

Examples from "Paul Revere's Ride"
lines 20–21 (p. 573)
Kind of Figurative Language simile
Effect on Mood and Meaning makes mood feel anxious, oppressive; shows British are "jailers"

lines 45–46 (p. 574)
Kind of Figurative Language simile
Effect on Mood and Meaning adds to feeling of suspense, secrecy; part of war theme

lines 97–100 (p. 576)
Kind of Figurative Language personification
Effect on Mood and Meaning Makes mood ominous; suggest war deaths to come

Examples from "The Cremation of Sam McGee"
line 14 (p. 595)
Kind of Figurative Language simile
Effect on Mood and Meaning shows cold is painful, extreme; suggests harm

line 18 (p. 595)
Kind of Figurative Language personification
Effect on Mood and Meaning shows night is clear; lightens mood

line 33 (p. 595)
Kind of Figurative Language metaphor
Effect on Mood and Meaning shows that speaker feels obligated to cremate friend

Choose a *figure of speech* from the chart. Explain the imaginative comparison it makes. Tell why you think the poet used it.
Possible answer: The night wind is compared to a sentinel, or watchful soldier. The poem is about the beginning of the Revolutionary War. Its characters are all focused on the approaching British army and how they must respond. The image is fitting both to the immediate action and to the idea of people fighting to guard liberty.

Reviewing Sound Devices

Why do poets use *sound devices*? Sound devices add musical effects that can underscore and enhance the meanings of words and mood of writing.

What are some of the effects of *sound devices*? Possible answer: Sound devices establish a rhythmic beat. They introduce the melody of rhyme and highlight the sound of repeated vowels or consonants. They can make a word sound like what it means.

1. rhyme
2. alliteration
3. meter
4. rhythm
5. consonance
6. onomatopoeia
7. rhyme scheme
8. foot
9. assonance

Applying Sound Devices in the Selections

Poem "The Choice"
Rhyme Scheme ababcdcd efefghgh
Description of Meter 4 feet per line; more syllables per foot in even numbered lines
Effects of Sound Devices on Poem Possible answer: sound devices keep the poem light

Poem "Casey at the Bat"
Rhyme Scheme aabb, ccdd, etc.
Description of Meter 7 feet per line; use of iambs
Effects of Sound Devices on Poem Possible answer: drives narrative; keeps pace lively

Poem "Paul Revere's Ride"
Rhyme Scheme rhyme scheme varies from stanza to stanza
Description of Meter 4 feet per line; mostly iambs
Effects of Sound Devices on Poem Possible answer: imitates drumming hoofbeats; adds to suspense

Poem "The Bat"
Rhyme Scheme aa bb cc dd ee
Description of Meter 5 feet per line; use of iambs
Effects of Sound Devices on Poem Possible answer: like formal speech; restrained description to match fear

Describe the rhythm of "Southbound on the Freeway." Is it written in meter? Explain your answer. Possible answer: The rhythm is much like analytical speech—measured, observing, rather slow. The lines vary in the number of syllables and stressed beats, so it does not have a strict meter.

> I <u>waited</u> twenty years,
> then <u>sailed</u> back, half <u>way</u> around the <u>world</u>.

Possible answer: Alliteration is evident in the repeated *w* sounds. The repetition of the a sound in *waited, sailed,* and *way* shows assonance. Both sound effects lengthen the sounds of words and slow down their pronunciation, which adds to a feeling of longing.

> There was no <u>angel</u> to warn me
> of the <u>dangers</u> of looking back.
> <u>Like</u> <u>Lot's</u> wife, I would trade
> my <u>living</u> blood for one <u>last</u> <u>look</u> …

Possible answer: *Angel* and *dangers* repeat vowel and consonant sounds. The sounds of these words build a sense of anxiety. Beginning *l* sounds repeat often (in *looking, like, Lot's, living, look*); this sound is liquid and has a smoothing influence.

> to <u>gaze</u> <u>again</u> on the fishermen of the bay
> <u>dragging</u> their catch in nets <u>glittering</u>
> <u>like</u> pirate <u>gold</u>, to the shore.

Meeting the Standards

Possible answer: In these lines, *g* and *l* sounds repeat (in *gaze, again, dragging, glittering, like, gold*). The combined hard and liquid sounds seem like little nuggets that emphasize the shining of the scene.

Practice Test

1. A	6. A	11. D	16. D
2. D	7. A	12. B	17. C
3. C	8. B	13. A	18. D
4. B	9. D	14. B	19. D
5. C	10. B	15. B	20. C

Southbound on the Freeway

Vocabulary: Latin Prefixes

A. 1. E
    2. A
    3. C
    4. B

    5. D
B. 6. transfusion
    7. transcribe
    8. transaction

    9. transmit
    10. transparent

Build Background: Highways in the 1960s

A. 1. the Federal-Aid Highway Act
    2. Dwight D. Eisenhower
    3. the automobile industry
    4. Interstate highways improved the mobility of military troops to and from airports, seaports, rail terminals, and other military bases.
    5. user fees, gasoline taxes, tolls collected on toll roads and bridges, federal government
B. 6. Answers will vary.
    7. Answers will vary.
    8. East-west highways have even numbers, and north-south highways have odd numbers.
    9. green
    10. with numbers

Analyze Literature: Connotation and Diction

A. 1. someone not invested in a place
    2. a small planet
    3. a life form
    4. being in some way superior

    5. indicating a mystery
    6. body parts
B. Possible paragraph:
    Swenson's vernacular diction is used to indicate a certain naïveté on the part of the alien, or "tourist," from Orbitville. The undiscerning observer in his spaceship parked above a freeway sees moving "metal and glass" shapes and falsely deduces these are the main creature of Earth. Tires appear as "round" feet, front and rear lights appear as eyes. The creature with "a red eye turning" is really a police car, which the alien sees as "special" because "others respect him/and go slow." The alien reaches arbitrary conclusions based on sensory input. The deadpan tone in which the observations are made underlines the simplicity of the alien in ascertaining who's really in charge on Earth. The poet shows life on Earth as being centered around the automobile—the "creature" itself, its body parts, its chosen path on "measuring tapes." The word "creature" indicates something that's alive, as if cars have a life of their own beyond what people use them for. The alien feels affinity with a machine-centered world, but the poet wonders, Is human reliance on machines and technology taking our human existence?

© EMC Publishing, LLC   *Meeting the Standards*   LEVEL III, UNIT 6   **97**

Use Reading Skills: Monitor Comprehension

1. alien
2. monologue
3. human
4. tires
5. freeway
6. car lights
7. police car
8. onomatopoeia
9. snake
10. people

Expository Writing

Paragraphs will vary.

Selection Quiz

1. B
2. C
3. A
4. A
5. C
6. A
7. B
8. C

Southern Mansion

Build Background: Antebellum South

1. in 1861 when the Civil War started
2. *Gone with the Wind*
3. Fugitive Slave Act
4. cotton, rice, corn, sugarcane, and tobacco
5. Answers will vary.
6. Rare; almost ninety percent of landowners owned twenty or fewer slaves.
7. The largest plantations had hundreds of slaves.
8. They played together.
9. They were often separated.
10. Slaves were considered property.

Build Background: Slave Narrative

A. Summaries will vary.
B. Answers will vary. This activity is designed to connect students to the theme of retribution in the poem.

Literary Connection: Literary Terms

A. 1. setting
2. symbol
3. onomatopeia
4. symbol

B. 5. theme
6. quiet
7. natural world
8. haunting

9. past and present
10. lives of slave owners and slaves

Use Reading Strategies: Make Inferences

A. 1. The slave owners are being described. The words *ladies, shade,* and *marble* indicate this. (White women protected their skin, which the culture said should stay fair.)
2. The music of the Big House is contrasted with the innocuous sound of "tinkling" in the cotton fields; this sound belies the suffering of the slaves.
3. The iron clank indicates finality.
4. The gate symbolizes the entrance into a lost world.
5. The verb "trembles" evokes fear.
6. The ghosts are the unquiet souls of the slaves who are exacting retribution for their mistreatment. Their trampling of the roses, symbols of the life of the southern aristocracy, is a mild retribution.

7. This line, which begins and ends the poem, points out that this era may be over but the poplars stand witness to the ghosts that still haunt the property.

B. Possible paragraph:
In "Southern Mansion," the poet Arna Bontemps contrasts the lives of the wealthy landowners, who live a life of privilege and leisure, with the lives of the slaves who were forced to work in the cotton fields. The speaker sees the ghosts of both groups and hears the "music echoing" from the parlor of the Big House and the "tinkling" of the slaves' chains in the fields. The gate in the last stanza symbolizes the entrance into this lost world. The ghosts of the slaves have trampled a symbol of the aristocratic life, the rose beds. The poplars are stable witnesses to the ghosts that still haunt the property and that demand retribution.

Expository Writing

A. 1. death
   2. restrained
   3. retribution
   4. objective
   5. nature

B. Paragraphs will vary.

Selection Quiz

1. A
2. B
3. A
4. B

5. B
6. A
7. B
8. B

9. A
10. A

Bats

Build Background: Myth or Fact?

A. Surveys will vary. Point out to students that their surveys will not be scientifically accurate reflections of teen viewpoints about bats. However, they will give an indication of teen opinions in your school's population.

B. 1. Myth; Bats are not flying rats; bats belong to the Chiropteras family, while rodents belong to the Rodentia family.
   2. Myth; Bats are not birds with fur; all birds have feathers.
   3. Myth; Bats are very clean; they even groom themselves like cats.
   4. Myth; Bats are very gentle and shy; they like to stay away from humans.
   5. Myth; While bats use echolocation at night to find or stay away from objects, they can see during the day if they need to.
   6. Myth; Most bats do not suck blood; however, there are three species of bats in South America that suck blood, usually that of livestock.
   7. Myth; Bats in the tropics are responsible for dispersing seeds and pollinating flowers.
   8. Myth: Bats try to stay away from people.

Use Reading Skills: Identify Author's Purpose

A. 1. B
   2. A
   3. D

4. E
5. C

B. Possible paragraph:
Randall Jarrell wrote "Bats" to educate people about bats and to dispel myths about them. He was probably most interested in educating children because he loved teaching. He once said, "If I were a rich man, I'd pay money to teach." In his poem, the reader learns about bats' nocturnal activities, how echolocation works, how bats sleep, how bat mothers care for their babies, and what it's like to be a baby bat. By focusing on the relationship between

a mother bat and her baby, Jarrell dispels many myths about bats as fearful and harmful to humans. In Jarrell's poem, bats deserve our attention and care just like any other mammal. He seems to personify bats in the last line: "[The mother bat] folds her wings about her sleeping child." Bats are concerned about their young like people. Jarrell hopes his poem will help people think differently about bats.

Poet's Attitude toward His Subject

A. 1. informed
   2. objective or subjective
   3. sympathetic
   4. respectful
   5. impressed

B. Possible paragraph:
Jarrell demonstrates that he is informed about the life of bats in his poem "Bats." He describes the nocturnal habits of bats, their use of echolocation at night, their sleeping habits, and their care of their young. Although objective about facts that pertain to bats, Jarrell can't help but let his sympathy and respect for bats come through. He describes the tenuous existence of a baby bat with sympathy: "He clings to her long fur/By his thumbs and toes and teeth." He shows his respect for bats when he paints an image in the night sky that dispels fearful myths about bats into an image of beauty: "Their single shadow, printed on the moon/Or fluttering across the stars,/Whirls on all night . . . " Jarrell is impressed by many things about bats, including how they sleep during the day: "Their sharp ears, their sharp teeth, their quick sharp faces/Are dull and slow and mild." Jarrell's attitude toward bats is based on science and observation, not on myths and superstitions like Roethke's poem.

Text-to-Text Connection

A. "Bats"
   1. like a bird flying through the night sky, revealing a silhouette against the moon and stars
   2. sleep hanging upside-down
   "The Bat"
   3. quick swooping movements that scare humans
   4. "mice with wings"

B. Possible paragraph:
While Jarrell focuses on what makes people wonder and marvel about bats, Roethke centers his attention on what makes people afraid of bats. Jarrell speaks with a voice of wonder when he paints a picture of how bats appear against the moon and stars: "Their single shadow, printed on the moon/Or fluttering across the stars,/Whirls on all night . . . " He marvels about how bats sleep upside-down: "They hang themselves up by their toes,/ They wrap themselves in their brown wings." Roethke, on the other hand, portrays bats as creatures that startle us when they brush up against a screen. He plays on the myth that bats are "mice with wings," even though he describes them as having a "human face." While Jarrell's poem looks at bats using the observational skills of a scientist, Roethke pokes fun at the bat in a light and playful way. Jarrell appears to admire and respect bats, while Roethke sees them as comical, sometimes fearful, creatures.

Selection Quiz

A. 1. yes
   2. yes
   3. yes
   4. yes
   5. no
   6. no
   7. yes
   8. yes

B. 9. F
   10. F
   11. F
   12. T
   13. T

The Choice

Build Background: My Partner

A. Answers will vary.
B. Paragraphs will vary.

Dorothy Parker's Life

1. unlucky
2. 1920s
3. New York
4. She made quotes.

5. alcohol
6. screenwriter
7. both
8. poet

9. luminaries
10. She stood up to men.
11. She lived a sad life.
12. She was successful professionally.

Vocabulary: Nuances

A. 1. "Fuming" would indicate that a smoke, vapor, or gas was emanating from the rubies. "Smoldering" is a better word choice because it also suggests passionate feelings.
2. "Spirited" indicates a personality more than a way of speaking. "Lilting" suggests she fell in love with the man's voice.
3. Both lace and satin suggest opulence and would have been appropriate gifts from her wealthy suitor, but lace suggests more artistry and an appreciation of quality imported artisan goods.
4. "Flickered" would indicate a light that went in and out, while "glimmered" suggests constancy, like the continuous shower of gifts the speaker would have received from the sweetheart described as "he."
5. "Luster" would indicate a glow of a light from within, while the poet wants to suggest the surface of a fabric. "Luster" would have indicated an inner glow the rejected sweetheart gave her, which was not the meaning she intended.

B. 6. sheen
7. lilting
8. flickered
9. lace
10. fuming

Analyze Literature: Make Judgments

1. The lover described as "he" was rich and generous.
2. The lover addressed as "you" is passionate and upbeat.
3. The speaker fell head-over-heels with the lover addressed as "you." She says, "You were sudden and swift and strong," indicating he swept her off her feet.
4. The gifts in lines 9–12 can be characterized as clothing and transportation.
5. The speaker says, "Gaily I followed wherever you led," indicating that the man was in charge and made the decisions in the relationship.
6. The last line of the poem makes it humorous. With its idiomatic expression, it contrasts sharply with the rest of the poem, which is a typical lyric poem about love, with elevated language, until the concluding line.

Text-to-Text Connection

A. 1. no
2. no
3. yes
4. no

5. yes
6. yes
7. no
8. yes

9. no
10. no

B. Possible paragraph:

"Love Song" and "The Choice" are similar in their humorous treatment of the topic of love. Both start out as typical lyric poems. In "Love Song" the last line of each stanza makes the poem humorous. In the first stanza, the speaker points out all the qualities of her lover, only to conclude, "And I wish I'd never met him." In the second stanza, the speaker attributes almost mythological characteristics to her lover, but then concludes, "And I wish he were in Asia." In the third stanza, the speaker characterizes her lover almost as a force of nature, but then concludes, "And I wish somebody'd shoot him." Obviously, she is only revealing the favorable qualities of her lover and it is up to the reader to guess what the lover could have done to so change the speaker's mind about him. In "The Choice" the last line of the second stanza makes the poem humorous. The speaker is writing about choosing between two lovers. The first, referred to as "he," is rich and generous and would have showered her with property, fine clothing, horses, and jewels. The second, addressed as "you," is happy-go-lucky and passionate, but lacking in material wealth. The speaker concludes, "Somebody ought to examine my head!" because she chose the poor suitor.

Selection Quiz

A. True or False
1. T
2. T
3. F
4. T
5. T

B. Multiple Choice
6. C
7. A
8. B
9. C
10. A

Ode to My Socks

Deduction: What Is an Ode?

1. Odes can be about people, objects, nature, or events.
2. Odes exalt.
3. Odes are reflective.
4. Odes exalt the chosen topic and reflect on it. Older odes have an elevated style and formal stanzaic structure. More modern odes are not so restricted in form.
5. Answers will vary.

Build Background: *Il Postino*

1. Pablo Neruda was exiled from Chile in 1949 and lived on the island of Capri in southern Italy for a time.
2. He believed in common people and wrote for them.
3. He widely used figurative language; for example, there are similes and metaphors in "Ode to My Socks."
4. He is widely known for his love poems.
5. He was a Communist, which got him into trouble with the government in Chile.

Vocabulary from Spanish Words

1. *manos*: hands
2. *pastora*: sheepherder
3. *modo*: way
4. *luminosos*: glowing
5. *impulso*: impulse
6. *manos*: manual, manufacture, manumission
7. *pastora*: pastorale, pastoral, pastor
8. *modo*: mode
9. *luminosos*: illuminated, illumine, luminous, illumination
10. *impulso*: impulse, impulsive

Use Reading Skills: Monitor Comprehension

1. B	4. B	7. B
2. A	5. B	8. A
3. B	6. A	9. A

Expository Writing

Paragraphs will vary.

Selection Quiz

A. Fill in the Blank	B. Multiple Choice
1. ambassador	6. A
2. Chile	7. B
3. teenager	8. B
4. senator	9. B
5. Nobel Prize	10. B

Casey at the Bat

Build Background: Baseball Quiz

A. Questions will vary.
B. Answers will vary.
C. Paragraphs will vary.

Literary Connection: Allusions

A. Students may say that there is much truth in the line from the poem "Essay on Criticism." It also clearly states a commonly-held belief.
B. Answers will vary.

Vocabulary: Synonyms

A. 1. ball	6. K	11. J
2. leather-covered sphere	7. E	12. A
3. spheroid	8. G	13. L
B. 4. F	9. B	14. H
5. I	10. C	15. D

Literary Connection: Narrative Events

A. 1. Cooney and Burrows don't get to stay on first base. (Stanza 1)
2. Blake is safe on second, and Flynn is safe on third. (Stanza 4)
3. Casey doffs his hat. (Stanza 6)
4. Casey misses his first hit. (Stanza 8)
5. The Mudville crowd gets angry at the umpire. (Stanza 9)
6. Casey ignores the second pitch. (Stanza 10).
7. Casey strikes out on his last hit. (Stanza 12)
8. There is no joy in Mudville. (Stanza 12)
B. See parentheses after sentences in Part A.

Analyze Literature: Parody

Possible paragraph:
In Garrison Keillor's parody of "Casey at the Bat," called "Casey at the Bat (Road Game)," the writer/radio host tells the same story but from the point of view of the opposing side, the Dustburg team and fans. Keillor uses the same *aabb* rhyme scheme in each stanza as Thayer. For example, in the second stanza, line one's last word is "clapped," which rhymes with "snapped" at the end of line two. Line three's last word is "lout," which rhymes with "out" at the end of line four. Keillor also parodies the events in Thayer's poem. The same players are up to bat--Cooney, Flynn, and Blake--to be followed by Casey, who is characterized as a "big fat ugly lout," a "bully and a braggart, a cretin and a swine," and a "pansy." He is no longer the hero of Mudville but a reviled opponent. Keillor's poem is longer than Thayer's by six stanzas and devotes more time to Casey at the bat. Keillor uses crude humor to parody the original poem. When Casey strikes out onto the grass, he scratches his ass. The fans of the Dustburg team make the sound of farting. The pigeons in the rafters crap and ruin all the beer. Casey spits tobacco juice. When Casey strikes out, they throw hot dogs down at him "and other souvenirs." They rub the doors and windows of the Mudville team's bus with "a special kind of cheese" that smells "like something died from an intestinal disease." In Keillor's version of the poem, the Casey at the bat story, known by all, is vilified for the lowest common denominator.

Selection Quiz

1. A
2. B
3. A
4. B

5. A
6. A
7. A

Paul Revere's Ride

Build Background: Colonial America

A. Descriptions will vary.
B. Paragraphs will vary.

Build Background: Revolutionary America in Fiction

A. 1. Esther Forbes; Howard Fast
   2. revolutionary Boston; revolutionary Lexington and Concord
   3. Johnny Tremain; Adam Cooper
   4. fourteen to sixteen; teenager
   5. pride (man versus himself) and injured hand (man versus man); feels his father doesn't love him (man versus himself) and war (man versus man)
   6. Johnny becomes more humble and finds a place for himself professionally. Adam resolves his issue with his father and becomes a man when his father dies in battle and he has fought in the first battle of the Revolutionary War.
   7. Paul Revere shows Johnny how to make a handle for a silver sugar basin. A midnight rider comes and says the British are coming, alerting the militia to prepare for battle.
B. Paragraphs will vary.

Colonial Lexicons

A. 1. moorings: a place where a ship can be made fast with anchors
   2. man-of-war: a British battleship
   3. mast: a long vertical pole that supports the rigging and sails of a ship
   4. spar: a pole that helps to support a ship's sail
   Additional vocabulary will vary.

B. 10. muster: gathering of soldiers to prepare for battle
   11. barracks: hall where soldiers gather and sometimes sleep
   12. grenadiers: infantry soldiers
   13. encampment: place where soldiers set up a camp
   14. sentinel: guard
   15. musket: large-caliber muzzle-loading firearm
   16. red-coats: British soldiers who wore a red uniform
   Additional vocabulary will vary.

Analyze Literature: Characterization

A. 1. Paul Revere makes a historic decision that will help him know if he should warn the colonists in Lexington and Concord. He tells his friend to hang one lantern if the British troops are marching by land or two lanterns if they're moving by ship.
   2. He is a man on a mission who doesn't care about his personal well-being.
   3. He pats the horse's side.
   4. He risks imprisonment by the British if he is caught.
   5. He carries out his mission just as he said he would.
B. Possible paragraph:
   Longfellow creates a favorable portrait of Paul Revere as decisive, fearless, a friend of animals, patriotic, and dependable. Paul Revere is decisive when he tells his comrade how to signal him on the opposite shore: "Hang a lantern aloft in the belfry arch/Of the North Church tower as a signal light,—/One, if by land, and two, if by sea . . . " He is fearless when he decides to take the risk to warn the colonists, unconcerned about his own well-being. He is a friend of animals when he pets the horse while awaiting the belfry signal. He is patriotic when he stands up against British oppression, even though he risks imprisonment if he is caught. He is dependable because he does what he told his comrades he would do. His "cry of defiance and not of fear" makes him a patriotic hero for the ages, and a symbol of liberty for all time.

Text-to-Text Connection

A. 1. To Longfellow, the Somerset, a man-of-war, symbolizes the might and force of the British army: "a huge black hulk, that was magnified/By its own reflection in the tide." All Forbes says is a fact: "There had been neither hail nor shot from the Somerset."
   2. The man who signals Revere in Longfellow's poem is anonymous. He is an important character, however, because it is he who sees the significance of his act of signaling and it is he who foreshadows the deaths at Lexington and Concord by contemplating the graveyard. He is not even mentioned in Forbes's account. She, however, mentions all the people with whom Revere came in contact that night who can be historically identified.
   3. In Longfellow's poem we don't get to know any of the British soldiers; the viewpoint is colonial. They are not personalized because they are the enemy. The only mention of the British in the historical account, besides mention of the Somerset, is this: "Nor would he wish to fling himself headlong into any trap set for him by that advance guard of officers . . . " With this line Forbes shows how dangerous Revere's mission is.
   4. According to Longfellow, Revere reaches Lexington at one o'clock, where the meeting-house windows seem to stare at him like a person, a witness to his heroic act. At two o'clock he reaches Concord, where the tranquil nature scene is unprepared for the deaths that will soon follow. In Forbes's account, she mentions it is eleven o'clock and Revere has twelve miles to get to Lexington, with Concord another six further on.
   5. In both selections Revere has a place in history. According to Longfellow, due to Paul Revere, people throughout American history will rise up and be alert for signs and messages to defend themselves in times of great danger. Forbes says, "So away, down the moonlit road, goes Paul Revere and the Larkin horse, galloping into history, art, editorials, folklore, poetry . . . "
B. Possible paragraph:
   Longfellow, the poet, imagines the scene the signal-giver sees from the belfry tower of the Boston church and what Revere saw and heard riding into Concord and Lexington. He has poetic license to fill in the gaps of historical facts in order to stir the imagination and emotions

of the reader. Forbes, on the other hand, is curtailed by what is historically known—the people Revere encountered that fateful night, the loan of the Larkin horse. She makes a reference to Longfellow's poem when she says, "So away, down the moonlit road, goes Paul Revere and the Larkin horse, galloping into history, art, editorials, folklore, poetry . . . " She, too, is moved by Revere's heroism, seeing him as "a symbol to which his countrymen can yet turn. Paul Revere had started on a ride which, in a way, has never ended."

Selection Quiz

1. B
2. A
3. B
4. B
5. A
6. B
7. B
8. B
9. A

Grandma Ling

Build Background: Family Resemblances

Answers will vary.

Vocabulary: Compound Adjectives

A.
1. joke-filled
2. densely-populated
3. tight-fisted
4. old-fashioned
5. sure-footed
6. dimly-lit
7. long-winded
8. good-looking
9. deep-sea
10. four-door

B. Sentences will vary.

Use Reading Skills: Draw Conclusions

1. The speaker was a child living in America. This is made apparent when she talks about her "backyard in Pennsylvania."
2. The speaker was interested in her Chinese roots when young. This can be inferred when the speaker says she was not strong enough to dig that hole as a child.
3. The speaker was probably in her twenties when she made her trip. She was a child when told to dig a hole to China and then waited twenty years after that.
4. The speaker went to China, the only foreign location referenced in the first stanza.
5. The speaker was first aware of her grandmother's presence when she heard "her slippered feet softly measure/the tatami floor with even step."
6. The grandmother has a "tatami floor" and an "aqua paper-covered door," which indicate a foreign location.
7. The speaker shares a physical resemblance with her grandmother: " . . . and there I faced/ my five foot height, sturdy legs and feet,/square forehead, high cheeks and wide-set eyes . . . "
8. The speaker sees herself in her grandmother, a version of what she will look like herself in fifty years.
9. The grandmother's son, the speaker's father, left Taiwan twenty-five years ago; he was "a quarter century away."
10. The speaker shows her love and respect for her grandmother by hugging her. It was her only way to express her deep emotion for her grandmother because they did not speak the same language.

Use Reading Strategy: Ask Questions

Questions will vary.

Meeting the Standards

Text-to-Text Connection

A. 1. "Grandma Ling": The speaker realized she looked just like her grandmother and could see what she would look like in fifty years. "My Mother Juggling Bean Bags": The speaker's mother was a joker, juggler, and prankster who brought fun into the household.
   2. "Grandma Ling": The speaker shows love and respect for her grandmother by hugging her. "My Mother Juggling Bean Bags": The speaker shows love and respect for his mother when he decides to learn to juggle oranges.
B. Paragraphs will vary.

Selection Quiz

1. B
2. A
3. B

4. A
5. B
6. A

7. A
8. B
9. A

Exile

Build Background: A Place I Didn't Want to Leave

A. Illustrations will vary.
B. Descriptions will vary.

Build Background: Claim Memories

A. Lists will vary.
B. Images will vary.
C. Poems will vary.

Analyze Literature: Allusions

A. Lot and his family are warned to escape the wicked cities of Sodom and Gomorrah, but not to look back when they flee. Lot's wife looked back and she was turned into a pillar of salt.
B. The speaker in the poem and Lot's wife look back at their former homes.
C. The speaker's birthplace is not an evil city that will be destroyed.
D. The poet brings up Lot's wife because she couldn't fight off a strong need to look back at the place that had been her home, like the speaker in "Exile."

Use Reading Strategies: Make Inferences

1. The speaker's birthplace is in a coastal area. From reading background information about Cofer's childhood, students should be able to identify it as the island of Puerto Rico.
2. The "cancelled postage stamp" indicates finality, just as the speaker cannot return to the island home of her childhood.
3. The speaker is like Lot's wife in that she can't resist looking back at the place that had been her home.
4. Cofer associates her family members with the house where she was brought up. She can still see their faces in the windows.
5. The image of the speaker strolling in the plaza in her Sunday best evokes the speaker's childhood innocence.
6. Cofer saw continuity in her future. She did not anticipate that she would be taken from her home. She and her friends imagined their children playing in the orchards "in the leisurely summer of our future."
7. The speaker wants to go home.
8. She is willing to have blood drained for her body and to lose future years of her life to return to her childhood home.

9. She is speaking figuratively.
10. Cofer has a golden memory of the fisherman. She lived in Puerto Rico as a child and her innocence and age kept harder realities of life on the island at bay. In her memory, Puerto Rico is a perfect place.
11. Her birthplace is a shell of what it used to be. Her word choice reflects death and decay.
12. Although she had two homes, Cofer preferred living in Puerto Rico to living in the United States.

Text-to-Text Connection

A. 1. lyric; lyric
   2. Puerto Rico; a plantation house in the South
   3. touch, sight; sight, sound
   4. innocent, golden, nostalgic; nature, refined, troubling, ghostly
   5. The past was innocent and filled with happy memories. The past was filled with refined accoutrements for the wealthy, pain and suffering for the slaves.
   6. The speaker is subjective about the past. The speaker is objective about the past and does not identify himself.
   7. Her happy childhood memories were there. The pain and suffering of the slaves live on.
B. Possible paragraph:
   "Exile" is a lyric poem about the childhood memories of the speaker in Puerto Rico. "Southern Mansion" is a lyric poem that shows how the past informs the present of a wealthy plantation home in the South. In "Exile," the senses of touch and sight bring Puerto Rico alive again for the speaker. Her past is innocent, golden, and she is nostalgic about her childhood. She says "my past clings to my fingers/so that every word I write hears/the mark like a cancelled postage stamp/of my birthplace." She remembers her family, seeing them in the windows of her childhood home "as in a family album." She remembers the plaza where she strolled on Sundays with her friends, thinking of a future with children on the island. She remembers the shoreline where the fishermen dragged "their catch in nets glittering/like pirate gold . . . " In "Southern Mansion," the senses of sight and sound bring the antebellum South alive in images of nature. The poplars stand "still as death." Feeling the presence of ghosts, a "dry leaf trembles on the wall." The music of the Big House contrasts with the "tinkling" of the bondmen's chains in the cotton fields. For the speaker of "Exile," the past was innocent and filled with happy memories. But in "Southern Mansion," the memories of the past are troubling, filled as they are with the pain and suffering of the slaves. In "Exile," the speaker is subjective and almost confessional about her past. The speaker in "Southern Mansion" removes himself from the images and descriptions. The speaker of "Exile" must remember Puerto Rico because all her happy childhood experiences were there. The speaker of "Southern Mansion" is haunted by the pain and suffering of the slaves whose ghosts won't let the past be forgotten.

Selection Quiz

1. A
2. B
3. A
4. B
5. A
6. A
7. B
8. B

Birdfoot's Grampa / The Time We Climbed Snake Mountain

Build Background

Students' answers will vary.

Set Purpose

"Birdfoot's Grampa" Possible answer:
What Title Suggests "Birdfoot" sounds like an American Indian name; "Grampa" is child's word. The speaker may be an American Indian child.
What Illustrations Suggest The poem will feature a serious American Indian man.
Possible Themes A grandfather deserves respect and should be listened to.

"The Time We Climbed Snake Mountain" Possible answer:
What Title Suggests The poem may be about two or more people climbing a mountain inhabited by snakes.
What Illustrations Suggest This poem will feature a large snake.
Possible Themes When climbing, be mindful of snakes.

Practice Vocabulary

1. a. chanced to see
   b. marked by spots
2. a. characterized by life; being alive
   b. dwell
3. a. clambered
   b. ascended
4. a. locations
   b. store or place of business

Compare Literature: Symbolism

"Birdfoot's Grampa" Possible answers:

Images/Actions	Associations
1. leaping toads blinded by headlights	part of nature; affected by civilization
2. stopping a car	being willing to give up convenience
3. lifting toads to safety	small, kind gesture
4. leathery hands	time spent outdoors, exposed to elements

"The Time We Climbed Snake Mountain" Possible answers:

Images/Actions	Associations
5. climbing a mountain	great effort; aspirations
6. moving carefully on a cliff	danger; vulnerability
7. nake sleeping in sun	cold-blooded; possible danger
8. bright sunshine	hot, bright day; life-giving energy

Compare Literature: Symbolism (continued)

"Birdfoot's Grampa" Possible answer:
Symbol toads
Details helpless and easily killed
What It Suggests It suggests a natural world that is often trampled by civilization.

"The Time We Climbed Snake Mountain" Possible answer:
Symbol snake
Details sleeping, owns the mountain
What It Suggests It suggests that the rightful owners of Earth are the wild creatures that have inhabited the planet for ages.

1. Both poems illustrate the importance of care for and awareness of the wild creatures in nature. Both suggest that learning to live with and not destroy nature is among life's most important aims.
2. Both poems include symbols of nature and wild creatures. The animal chosen in each case is one that many people fear and dislike or feel is of little value.

Compare Literature: Imagery

"Birdfoot's Grampa" Possible answers:

Imagery
1. toads blinded by lights, "live drops of rain"
2. misty rain on white hair
3. leathery hands full of wet brown toads

Effect of Imagery
4. humble, common, vulnerable
5. natural, enveloped in wetness
6. shared color, roughness of "skin"
7. sense of a bond between the man and nature

"The Time We Climbed Snake Mountain" Possible answers:

Imagery
8. warm handholds on cliffs
9. snake with yellow spots, sleeping
10. slab of rock exposed to sun

Effect of Imagery
11. warmth, life emphasized
12. vulnerability
13. warm colors, sensations
14. sense that the mountain is a good place for all to be

Write a paragraph to compare and contrast the imagery from these two poems. Use the information from your chart in your answer. Possible answer: "Birdfoot's Grampa" presents vivid images of a considerate old man lifting toads out of a rainy roadway so they won't be killed. "The Time We Climbed Snake Mountain" describes several people slowly climbing a steep mountain in the hot sun, while a patterned snake sleeps comfortably nearby. In both poems, the images focus on the elements and a creature most people would like to avoid. Both show that the creatures are vulnerable and at the mercy of humans. Both poems also use color (brown and yellow) to tie together the parts of the poems. However, in the first poem, rain and brown dominate and subdue the mood. In the second, glaring sunlight and yellow dominate and lighten the mood.

Use Reading Strategies: Make Connections

Text-to-Text   Possible answer: Both characters are grandfathers who see negative influences in the "civilized" world. Each man tries to pass a lesson on to an impatient grandchild (the narrator/speaker). Birdfoot's grampa can demonstrate his lesson of compassion through actions. In "The Medicine Bag," Grandpa is weak and must tell his lesson through story.

Text-to-Self   Students' answers will vary.

Text-to-World   Students' answers will vary.

Focus on "Birdfoot's Grampa"

Mirrors & Windows Question
Students' answers will vary.

Selection Quiz
1. image
2. figure of speech
3. image
4. image
5. a car
6. leaping into the road
7. to move the toads out of harm's way
8. get back in the car
9. creates danger for frogs
10. Possible answer: He feels protective of the toads' lives. This and his words suggest that he believes that the toads' lives are important and deserving of respect.

Meeting the Standards   © EMC Publishing, LLC

Focus on "The Time We Climbed Snake Mountain"

Mirrors & Windows Question

Students' answers will vary.

Selection Quiz

1. the speaker
2. snake
3. the speaker
4. mountain
5. mountain
6. C
7. A
8. C
9. B
10. D

What Do You Think?

Students' answers will vary.

The Cremation of Sam McGee

Practice Vocabulary

1. brawn
2. marge
3. code
4. remains
5. grisly
6. boiler
7. moil
8. mushing
9. derelict
10. planks

Analyze Literature: Narrative Poetry

Exposition	Sam McGee from Tennessee suffers in the frigid North.
Rising Action	On a cold Christmas Day, McGee predicts he will die and makes the speaker promise to cremate him. He dies. Speaker transports the body for days until he finds a wrecked ship with a boiler.
Climax	Speaker builds fire and puts Sam McGee inside.
Falling Action	Speaker walks away, waits for a while, and returns.
Resolution	Speaker peeks inside and sees McGee revived and warm.

Analyze Literature: Meter

˘ ˘ / ˘ / ˘ ˘ / ˘ / ˘ ˘ / ˘ ˘ / ˘ /

Now a pro|mise made | is a debt | unpaid, | and the trail | has its own | stern code.

˘ ˘ / ˘ / ˘ ˘ ˘ / ˘ / ˘ ˘ / ˘ ˘ / ˘ /

In the days | to come, | though my lips | were dumb, | in my heart | how I cursed| that load.

1. seven
2. The first, third, fifth, and sixth feet contain 2 unstressed syllables followed by 1 stressed syllable. The second, fourth, and seventh feet contain 1 unstressed syllable followed by 1 stressed syllable.
3. Possible answer: The meter gallops and imitates the pace of the sled and dogs. It is vigorous and exciting. It suits the handling of the legendary subject.

Selection Quiz

1. the Alice May
2. Lake Lebarge
3. Plumtree, Tennessee
4. Dawson trail
5. Lines 1–2 and lines 3–4 of each stanza rhyme.
6. in the first half of every line
7. Repeated *h* and *r* sounds are alliteration; *ou* sounds are assonance.
8. simile
9. B
10. C
11. A
12. D

Describe and Critique: Poetry

Title   "The Cremation of Sam McGee"
Author   Robert Service
Type of Poem   Narrative

Poetic Form   metrical and formal, with a regular pattern of rhyme
Line: 7 stressed beats per line
Stanza: quatrains

How Form Affects Meaning Possible answer: The rhythm and rhyme set a quick, suspenseful pace that makes the story dramatic. The meter mimics the racing of the sled dogs.

Use of Figurative Language, Imagery, Sound Effects Possible answers:

1. some similes and personifications: cold "like a driven nail"; heavens scowl; stars dance
2. colorful descriptions: frozen lashes; howling huskies; hot sweat; greasy smoke
3. strict meter: 7 feet per line; same number stressed/unstressed syllables per line
4. strict rhyme scheme: *aabb*; internal rhyme begins each line; lots of alliteration

Effect on Mood and Meaning: Possible answer: The language creates a dramatic musical effect. The poem sounds as if it should be read aloud.

Summary of Poem's Meaning

This poem is a fanciful account of a prospector carrying out his final promise to a friend (cremation). The surprise ending contains humor, as the intense fire thaws and revives the friend.

Critique, or review and evaluate, the poem "The Cremation of Sam McGee." Answer these questions.

Students' answers will vary.

Nikki-Rosa

Practice Vocabulary

1. a thing that ruins enjoyment
2. strongly desired goal
3. difficult
4. to roast over a heat source

5. shares of a corporation
6. were present at
7. multipurpose container of wood or metal
8. memories

During Reading Questions

Title **Use Reading Strategies: Make Predictions** I think the poem is about the poet. Her family might have called her Nikki-Rosa when she was a little girl. The title identifies the speaker with her personal history.

Line 6 **Use Reading Skills: Draw Conclusions** "They" are people who interview the speaker and try to write her life story. She doesn't want them to reduce her early life to its difficulties. She doesn't think they understand the experiences of African Americans.

Lines 9–11 **Analyze Literature: Imagery** Images give the home a feeling of closeness and warmth. They stress the speaker's appreciation of the simple pleasures of daily life.

Lines 18–19 **Use Reading Strategies: Evaluate Cause and Effect** The father had to sell what the family had invested for the future because they were experiencing financial troubles. As a result, the family had to let go of "another dream" for their future.

Lines 29–30 **Analyze Literature: Theme** The speaker says that African-American families are rich with love, but fears that observers won't understand this. The lines stress the speaker's belief that love and family are more valuable than money.

Analyze Literature: Speaker and Meaning

Details
Possible responses: assumes she will become famous
happy memories about time with mother, bath time
remembers that family was together to celebrate
concern for father's pain, disappointment

Main Idea
Possible responses: The speaker is a person who values closeness of family and their love for each other more than money.

Explain how the conclusion helps you understand the meaning of the poem. Possible responses: Details in "Nikki-Rosa" reveal that the speaker remembers her childhood as rich in love and family togetherness. She seems annoyed that biographers focus on childhood poverty. Her attitude helps me understand that to the speaker, "Black love is Black wealth"—happiness comes from love, not having money or things.

Use Reading Strategies: Make Connections

Text-to-Text   Possible answer: "Nikki-Rosa" is a free verse lyric poem that relies on imagery and a conversational style to make its point. Its loose structure and plain talk are suitable to the subject of fond family memories. "The Cremation of Sam McGee" is a narrative poem with a strict meter and rhyme scheme that increase the drama of the story. The quick pace and steady beat suit the dramatic situation of the topic.

Text-to-Self   Students' answers will vary.

Describe and Critique: Poetry

Title "Nikki-Rosa"
Author Nikki Giovanni
Type of Poem lyric

Poetic Form free verse
Line: long and short lines alternate randomly
Stanza: not divided into separate stanzas; 32 lines long

How Form Affects Meaning Possible answer: The free flowing form is suitable to the speaker's conversational language and informal family lifestyle.

Use of Figurative Language, Imagery, Sound Effects Possible answers:

1. imagery is main element; it creates pictures of simple, humble home with lots of celebrating, fighting, and ultimately warm emotions
2. does not use similes, metaphors, etc.
3. does not use rhyme or regular meter
4. very spare use of alliteration; some repetition (remember, happy, never understand)

Effect on Mood and Meaning: The language is very conversational; the speaker sounds like a regular person.

Summary of Poem's Meaning Families may be poor and go through hard times, but that doesn't keep them from being happy if they share a loving relationship.

Critique, or review and evaluate, the poem "Nikki-Rosa." Answer these questions.

Students' answers will vary.